THE UNFINISHED RACE

THE UNFINISHED RACE:

REDEFINING THE RECOVERY PROCESS

KYLENE COCHRANE

NEW DEGREE PRESS

THE UNFINISHED RACE:

Redefining the Recovery Process

ISBN 978-1-63676-870-0 *Paperback*

978-1-63730-172-2 *Kindle Ebook*

978-1-63676-345-3 *Ebook*

I Was an Actress.
In The Beginning, I Gambled with Guilt,
and was Provided Healing Words.
I held an Obsessive Identity until
I discovered a New Mindset,
And became Energized.
Reflecting on my Younger Misconceptions,

I Listened with Grace.
I utilized Mental Imagination.
Becoming Selfishly Selfless
I found my Present Identity.
I re-lived My Last Run
And unveiled the Life in the Between.

TABLE OF CONTENTS

To my family and friends who believed in this book
even before it was written, I thank you.

INTRODUCTION:

"Are you aware that you've been running in men's sneakers... and they are also a size too big?" From the beginning, my origins in running stemmed from innocence. My first taste for running began in middle school after not making the soccer team. I called my friend that afternoon to see if the cross-country team was still taking athletes. A few days later I found myself on the bus heading to a meet, and after the race I called my parents to tell them I had won. "You what?" My parents were as surprised as I was.

Those were my golden days of running: when running was novel and innocent like the wrong-sized sneakers I wore for two years. During my freshman year of high school, I was officially initiated into the world of track. In my first race, I saw the innocence of the sport in full display as I waved to my dad each lap, and also yelled enthusiastically, "Okay, coach," after he yelled my splits to me for each lap.

Today, that innocence is lost. At eighteen, I was the 1600-meters New Jersey State Champion. I then spent four years competing as a Division I collegiate track athlete at the University of Pennsylvania. During that time, I realized how much I missed those wrong-sized sneakers and the time in my life when I wasn't so swarmed by the "running" world.

I started writing this book in November of 2014, after enduring my first running injury in college. Sitting in my single dormitory room on Penn's campus, I let tears of despair mottle the first page I had barely filled. I heard the shouts and laughter of other students outside my window. I felt the pen beneath my hands while fully surrendering to the pain radiating from my leg, a relentless reminder that I was injured. I wasn't sure if this book would ever be a reality.

Sitting in the corner of my dimly lit dorm room, I felt something was wrong with me. "Why am I feeling this way?" I had lost a core aspect of my identity, and I did not know how to adapt. I felt alone and isolated, and my mind was suffering more than my injured leg. Intuitively I knew that my solitary, damaged image needed to be acknowledged, and I also knew I was not the only individual to have felt this way. The running world is far from perfect, and conversations surrounding the health of the complete athlete need to begin. There is a lack of focus on the mental psyche of injuries, and yet a heightened, unspoken focus on body image. These topics are silent, but they are there living and harming today's runners, and if not addressed, tomorrow's as well.

The year is 2021, and I decided I had to finish the story I began so long ago. Prior to picking up the pen, however, I was inspired by Mary Cain, a former professional runner. At seventeen years old, Mary Cain was among the fastest female runners in America and signed with a top professional running team.[1] To gain a spot on a professional sports team

---

1 *The New York Times*, "I Was the Fastest Girl in America, Until I Joined Nike | NYT Opinion," November 7, 2019, Youtube Video, 6:59.

is the epitome of love and passion intertwined into a job. According to the 2018-2019 NCAA Recruiting Facts, fewer than 2 percent of collegiate athletes go on to the professional level.[2] And yet, this is every athlete's dream.

The fact that a professional runner walked away from what others dream of depicts something about the running culture. Mary Cain left the highest level, professionalism, which was the maximum, the apex, the golden wish. Cain dared to do something that few people have the courage to do.

Her story is inspiring, but I wondered if it was unique or part of a larger trend. I wondered if faults in the running world were outside of the professional world and on the tracks of high schools and colleges. I set out to talk to runners and decided to make my return back into the world of competitive running.

I wanted to understand if other athletes felt the mental burden of injuries the way that I did.
I wanted to know if they struggled with body image.
I wanted to know how educated they were on the female body.
I wanted to know the life of runners within the running world.

Today, the current view of the running world lacks a holistic viewpoint. There is a strong focus on the run and very little on the environment and life surrounding the athlete. Attending a track meet, you hear shouts of encouragement, mile split times, and cadences to strive for. What about the identity one holds apart from the accumulation of miles?

2 "NCAA Recruiting Facts: College Sports Create a Pathway to Opportunity for Student-Athletes," National Collegiate Athletic Association, revised August 2020.

Society is led to believe the best runner is the fastest runner—the one who wins the meets, and the one who wears the golden medal. Athletes believe they are invincible; they will never get hurt. But athletes also continue to undermine the fact that their current choices will impact their health years later. It is not so much athletes pushing past their capabilities; it is athletes pushing past what is considered a healthy passion without even knowing it.

As a runner in both high school and at the D1 collegiate level, I was surrounded by the high intensity of the track culture, the long miles, and the timed runs. I was aware of the times and athletes around me, but I was at a complete loss and understanding as to what was occurring in my own body. I was internally breaking. I was running fast—but unconsciously was not energizing my body enough. I did not understand energy or viability. I was not nurturing my body. I was not loving it. I was not listening to it. My body broke five different times in college, and while my body continued to break, my mentality could only think of the end race.

People have asked me why I kept trying. Why? Behind the scenes, I could not give up. I told myself I would work hard those four years at Penn, learn as much as I could about myself, my body, and the extent of human grit, and then take a hiatus from running. I am now attending graduate school, working toward my doctorate of physical therapy. I am telling this story because I want to educate athletes now.

I believe the best runner is not the fastest runner.
I believe more mileage does not mean more success.
The running world has become a race to finish without preparing to start.

I want to first state a caveat; in no way are my recommendations, thoughts, or feelings in this book absolute. I am not recommending any particular medical advice. I am simply teaching the power of mindful and physical nurturing. I am simply empowering injury as a time to heal.

This book is broken into two parts, the first part addressing the mental components of injury, and the second considering how valuable a holistic identity is, rather than just an athletic one. This book particularly targets female athletes, especially runners, but can be read by any individual enduring their own injury. This book is not my story alone and encompasses interviews from other previously injured athletes. These athletes are not professionals, but rather everyday, passionate individuals. This story is an open memoir, a letter on what is not talked about enough, and the need to identify the actor/actress inside us all performing as if we are okay when in reality we are not.

PART ONE

THE BEGINNING

CHAPTER ONE:

I WAS AN ACTRESS

I was an actress. Even prior to taking the class "Intro to Acting," I discovered I consistently masked my emotions out of fear for vulnerability. It was the spring semester of my senior year at the University of Pennsylvania, and I had already committed to Drexel University's physical therapy graduate program. I was done with the heavy science-packed classes and decided to branch away from my comfort zone by enrolling in this class.

I signed up with hesitation because apart from class presentations, I never volunteered for absolute vulnerability. I personally felt comfortable sitting in the front of a classroom, taking diligent notes, while the professor displayed themself in front of me.

Day one of the class challenged me in a way that was far different from my neuroscience classes. I was called upon to make uninterrupted eye contact with a complete stranger for minutes straight. I found this incredibly difficult, but our professor persistently taught the secret behind unveiling true acting: trust and connection.

"I think I am going to drop the class," I told my friends later that day at track practice. I was able to pass molecular neurobiology, but I was not able to make eye contact with someone for minutes straight. I questioned, what does this say about grades and education? The fact that I can perform well on a GPA standard, but yet I failed to allow someone to search deep into my eyes. What was I afraid might be uncovered?

I went to the second class, and again, we were told to make eye contact. This time, however, there was a slight twist. Apart from just making eye contact, we had to tell our partner what we saw. "Your eyes are beautiful," my partner said, "and when you smile, your lips are uneven, but full, which is nice."

This was something I had never even noted about myself. The class continued to challenge me, and I began to appreciate making eye contact for prolonged periods of time. I felt my confidence grow, noting my ability to speak with purpose rather than ramble on, lost in my own words. I allowed individuals to stare at me, no longer feeling the need to hide away. I was growing comfortable in and appreciative of my own body.

"Your next assignment is different. I want you to act out a scene from your everyday life. This can include studying at the library or even riding a bike. But there is a caveat. You cannot use any words." Our mid-semester assignment had many of my classmates uncertain with regard to which scene they wanted to display. I knew the exact scene in my head; I had lived it far too many times.

For the day of my scene, I drew certain images I would tape to the wall on a few pieces of paper. I packed the drawings and arrived at class. Prior to each scene, the student stood in a small room next to our classroom and then opened the door as if they were arriving to their scene. After a few of my classmates went, I was told it was my turn.

Rising from my seat, I stepped into a newly casted energy as I felt everyone's eyes on me. Despite my racing heart and my clammy palms, I was ready. I put on my backpack and walked over to the plastered cement walls to hang up the few images I had. Stepping through the door that my professor told us to start behind, I closed the door and collected myself. I paused for a few minutes in the darkened room, taking a deep breath and molding my hand to the doorknob in front of me. This scene I was about to enact was all too familiar, and it pained my insides. I was still in so much discomfort with my past.

SCENE:

I open the door, headphones hanging around my neck, hands juggling the many bags I carry on campus. **I arrive to the doctor's office.**

Placing my bags on the chair, I walk over and look at the images on the wall. The room is dimly lit, it's cold, and my body is responding to nervousness by staring blankly at the image of the knee anatomy on the wall. Stepping back from the wall, my leg hits the plinth of the table by accident, and I nervously sit down. Minutes pass and there is still no knock on the door from the doctor, so I decide to lie down. As this distressing routine plays out, I put my headphones in my ears to listen to music. I decide to play some soft Taylor Swift so my melancholy emotions could at least be in parallel with something. I feel sad, my stomach aches, and I fear what the doctor will tell me. I feel pain, both in my mind and heart, as this waiting game is something I have grown to dread. I am reliving the memory, the salience, the purgatory of dread that came with each doctor's visit. I am touching the pain I've hidden away, and at this moment I am carefully grasping this present emotion while synonymously accepting my past.

END SCENE:

I hear clapping, and my scene is over. I am stunned back to reality. No longer was I patiently laying on the table at the doctor's office. I collected myself, calmed myself, and slowly got off the table to go sit with my classmates.

"I have never seen you look so serious," my friend told me. After my scene, I had to remove myself for a bit and go to the bathroom. I had hidden my emotions for such a long time that when I saw my watery eyes and blotchy skin in the mirror of the bathroom, I could only feel immense gratitude and relief.

Intro to Acting provided me a form of vulnerability. By reliving the dreaded emotions I felt in doctor's offices, I left my past and I arrived back to the present. I felt replenished, lighter, almost weightless, as I could fully accept my past without feeling guilty. Doctor's offices always filled me with regret, guilt, and bad news. Reliving that doctor's office scene allowed me to feel and process just my emotions. I was not awaiting an answer from a doctor, nor was I awaiting in hopeful anticipation clearance to run. It was through acting that I birthed my vulnerability, and I felt immensely blessed.

To be fully transparent, I was already an actress even prior to taking Into to Acting. I consistently tried my best to reflect positivity all the time, as I wanted to give off this perception that everything would be okay...that I was okay. It is remarkable to realize how alive I feel having awakened and validated those emotions I had masked and hidden for so long.

I am now able to talk about my injuries, my running career experience, and not feel pained by it. Never would I have believed that I needed a form of art to inculcate running back into my life again as something peaceful, content, and unharmed. Allowing ourselves to relive an experience that challenged us is pure validation, and with that knowledge, it is hoped we can become mentally stronger.

It took me four years to feel at peace with my injuries. I only wish I would have immersed myself into my emotions and validated them sooner. I know I am not alone in these emotions and fears, and I know the pain I felt exists, nags, and echoes in the minds of many runners and athletes. My hope after writing this book is that the mental burden of injuries receives more light.

In the running world especially, injuries are so common. There are two ways to approach assessing injuries. First, understanding the mental psyche of injuries. Secondly, from a preventative medicine standpoint that looks into seeing running from a holistic place. However, this is not the first time the running world needs a change, and I want to demonstrate to you how impactful change is, no matter what time period we are in. Before continuing forward in this book, I want to take you back a few decades, to a time when women were facing their own kind of societal injury that inhibited their ability to run—their fight for the right to race.

CHAPTER TWO:

THE HISTORY OF FEMALE RUNNING

Imagine: It is a beautiful day outside. There is not a cloud in the sky, and the temperature is sitting around 72 degrees. Your legs feel better than they have in weeks, and your weekly mileage logbook indicates you have a four-mile easy run. Lacing up your sneakers, you begin the warm-up in your driveway. Taking out your iPhone, you peruse Spotify, trying to find a song that will provide the perfect mood for the run. As you are looking through the top hits of 2021, your mom asks if you can bring in the mail before you leave. Breaking contact from Taylor Swift's name on your screen, you see a letter is addressed to you. Opening it, you read...

Dear _____,

We regret to inform you, but you are physiologically unable and incapable of running today. You are not allowed. Thank you and goodbye.

What would you do?

Run anyway?

Well, that is exactly what Roberta Gibb did in 1966, after receiving a letter in response to her application for the Boston Marathon, stating women were physiologically unable to race the marathon.[3]

The difficult history of female running does not receive enough attention. Women of the past had to fight for their equality in both the Olympics and the Marathon. Roberta Gibb was the first woman to complete the Boston Marathon and represent how physically capable women truly are.[4] Before we consider women's fight to run the marathon, we should consider their struggles to run on the world stage, at the Olympics, on an international, global scale.

In 1928, less than 100 years ago, women were finally able to participate in track and field at the Olympics, with the longest event being the 800m.[5] Women were seen as incapable of competing in longer-distance events, with an assumption that longer events were too physical for women.[6] This conclusion was reached after several women collapsed at the finish due to exhaustion.[7] In my opinion, this showed how gritty the women were, leaving everything out there on the track!

Afterwards, the president of the International Olympic committee considered removing women's running

---

3 *CBS Boston*, "A Boston Marathon First: Bobbi Gibb On Her History-Making Run," March 29, 2016, YouTube video, 3:09.

4 Charlie Lovett, *Olympic Marathon: A Centennial History of The Games' Most Storied Race* (Westport: Praeger Publishers, 1997), 126.

5 Charlie Lovett, *Olympic Marathon: A Centennial History of The Games' Most Storied Race* (Westport: Praeger Publishers, 1997), 125.

6 Charlie Lovett, *Olympic Marathon: A Centennial History of The Games' Most Storied Race* (Westport: Praeger Publishers, 1997), 125.

7 Charlie Lovett, *Olympic Marathon: A Centennial History of The Games' Most Storied Race* (Westport: Praeger Publishers, 1997), 125.

competition from the games altogether.[8] This did not ensue, but instead a rule was initiated that the longest race allowed was the 200 meters. It was not until 1960 that the 800-meter race returned.[9]

In 1966, the Boston Marathon still did not allow women to participate. Roberta Gibb is one of the females who fought to change these standards, and it was purely out of her love for running: *"I have a mind, and I want to do things, and here I was following this love for no reason; I wasn't even aware that I was going to make a social statement at that point."*[10]

Gibb awaited the start of the Boston Marathon by extraordinarily hiding behind a bush.[11] At the sound of the starter's pistol, Roberta jumped out from behind the bush to begin the journey that would embed her name into running history. Crossing that finish line was not just Gibb's accomplishment; it was a statement that demonstrated how physiologically capable women are for long-distance racing.

During this time, other pioneering women continued to run and fight for equality in the running world. In 1972, it was stated that women were finally allowed to compete in the Boston Marathon.[12]

During the 1980 Summer Olympics, a women's Olympic marathon race was still not contemplated. One reason included the assumption that long-distance running would

---

8 Ibid.

9 Ibid.

10 *CBS Boston*, "A Boston Marathon First: Bobbi Gibb On Her History-Making Run," March 29, 2016, YouTube video, 3:09.

11 Ibid.

12 Charlie Lovett, *Olympic Marathon: A Centennial History of The Games' Most Storied Race* (Westport: Praeger Publishers, 1997), 126-127.

negatively impact women's health.[13] Despite this false data, the Olympic Charter further stated an Olympic event could only be implemented if at least twenty-five countries practiced the sport on a minimum of two different continents.[14] The focus was on popularity of the women's marathon, and not on their right to race.[15]

So the fight for women's equality in the running world continued. Jaqueline Hansen in 1979 organized the International Runners Committee to advocate for women's long-distance races at the international level.[16]

With further leadership and persistence from pioneer women, the women's marathon was approved to be included in the 1984 Olympic Games.[17] It was not until 1991, however, not that long ago, that full gender equality was implemented in the Olympics, as any new sport considered for the Olympics is required to include women's events.[18] This was a huge moment for women's rights and represented the importance of having both women and men equally participating in international sports events.

The history of female running has granted me an appreciation and admiration for the sport of running. As a runner myself, I appreciate the work women before me did to provide all of us with this opportunity. I have been participating

---

13 Charlie Lovett, *Olympic Marathon: A Centennial History of The Games' Most Storied Race* (Westport: Praeger Publishers, 1997), 127.

14 Ibid.

15 Charlie Lovett, *Olympic Marathon: A Centennial History of The Games' Most Storied Race* (Westport: Praeger Publishers, 1997), 128.

16 Ibid.

17 Charlie Lovett, *Olympic Marathon: A Centennial History of The Games' Most Storied Race* (Westport: Praeger Publishers, 1997), 130-131.

18 "Statistics: Women at the Olympic Games," Olympic.org, accessed January 2, 2020.

in the sport for over eight years, and yet I was unaware of how hard women fought for my ability to run. Lacing up my spikes each race, I was focused on my future race time and not the historic time women spent making this race possible. I realize now the importance of advocating for change, no matter what time period we are in.

The year is now 2021, and I asked myself, does the running world need to change again? Running seems simple, but I argue there is so much still neglected. Between the step length of each run is both the before and the after, the aspects of our running journey that are left unwritten once we cross the finish line. What do we do before our run? What do we do after? How do we approach the run as an aspect of our life, but not the sole identity of it? The running world *has* changed, and it needs to change again.

The female pioneers of the running world fought for us to run, and now we owe it to one another to advocate for change again. This time, a different kind of change: understanding the holistic runner.

A PUSH FOR A NEW RUNNING WORLD:

The running world is consumed with the idea of fast. However, with our greater medical knowledge today, there are other thresholds athletes must consider apart from just posted mile times: energy levels, menstrual cycles, eating disorders, body image, training errors, and stress levels. All these elements impact a female athlete. Yet, there is an eerie quietness surrounding some of these topics.

Having been a runner myself at both the high school and collegiate level, I understand this. In high school, I went from winning races and being a state champion to becoming a sidelined athlete with an injury in college. I was naive to my limitations and my own personal body. Through these injuries I became aware of what can change, and so, I began advocating for and educating young athletes.

I chose not to interview professional athletes for this book. I wanted to interview the everyday runner, the athletes every individual can relate to. We do not receive a salary for running, and so our desire to run comes from pure passion alone. There is something rooted deep within us that needs to run.

I have endured many emotions. I learned aspects of running and of the female body that I never knew in high school. Stepping foot onto the UPenn track meant I was immersing myself in the truth of female athletes and injuries, and I was my own primary source. Some individuals may believe that as a D1 athlete at an Ivy League School, I was a success—that I made it to this pivotal moment and everything else would fall into place. This was not the case.

As a way to advocate for change, I want to show you the life behind social media, and the life only I knew existed. I did struggle, but these struggles led me to understand the mental components of injury and to learn how to be a holistic athlete. **I want to show you the beginning, the part of my life where I discovered the impact injury has on the mind.** Read on to learn the beginning of it all...my first injury: my femoral stress fracture.

CHAPTER THREE

THE BEGINNING

Injury: Femoral Stress Fracture.
Year: Freshman Year 2014.

I was a first-year college student who was truly struggling. I received the results from my biology midterm, and I failed it. Since I failed the exam, I was required to go to a review session on studying tactics. Walking back from the review session, I sloshed through snow while trying to cover my face from the heavy hail beating hard against it. I couldn't help but compare today to a year ago, my birthday, when I was crossing the finish line to a New Jersey 1600m State Championship title. *Happy birthday to me.*

Walking through the slush with my hat saturated with icy water and my curly hair frizzing out the sides, I hoped this was rock bottom. I had come to the University of Pennsylvania with pure excitement. The beautiful buildings, the prestigious institution, and the intelligent minds walking throughout campus filled me with anticipation. On the day I moved in, I put a UPenn baseball hat on my dad's dashboard. I was the first in my family to ever attend college, so when I showed up to move-in day with all six of my family members and way too many pieces of luggage, I knew I was going to be slightly different from some of my peers.

My differences came from my lack of knowledge about how to appropriately study in college. What I did in high school no longer worked in college. When I received an email that I failed my biology midterm, I panicked...I was worried I would fail the class. The next email I received was from a Penn advisor suggesting I attend a seminar on how to transition into different study habits for college. This made me feel better because I now had a plan.

The day of the seminar was also the day of the Heptagonal Winter Championships. This was the big winter track meet all of the Ivy League schools participated in. The reason why my schedule was free and I was able to go to the seminar was because I was injured. I came off the fall 2014 cross-country season with a femoral stress fracture.

My birthday a year prior, however, was immensely different. I was a senior in high school and was crowned a New Jersey Winter 1600-meter champion in track and field. Looking back on my senior year, I feel blessed. The fall was slightly stressful due to recruiting calls coming from coaches to schedule official visits, but once I made my decision to attend the University of Pennsylvania, I felt everything was finally falling into place. That Christmas, I opened boxes where the red and blue of Penn were clearly displayed, and I felt both optimistic but fearful at the same time.

I was undefeated that winter season in the 1600-meter, with my training including no speed workouts and just base mileage. Running-wise, I didn't overthink it. I loved running as the sun was slowly setting. There was something soothing about finishing a run just as the sun was finished with the day. I was also driving my dad's old Dodge Nitro at the time and the only radio station that came in was the local religious music channel. One of my favorite songs came from that radio station. Prior to each race I would listen to that song on my warm-up...It reminded me that it was just a race.

That senior year I qualified to run in Millrose Games. The Millrose Games is a historic track meet held at the Armory in New York City. A range of athletes attend the meet, from high school to professional runners. The caveat, however, was that this was the same day as New Jersey's Group meet. In New Jersey, athletes have to place top six in their event at groups to move on to Meet of Champions. Not attending the group meet would mean I could not move on to the Meet of Champions. I chose to run in Millrose over competing at my Group meet. I felt Millrose Games was a once-in-a-lifetime meet. The race came and went, and although it was definitely a great experience, I was just another runner in a big race.

The day of the New Jersey group meet, however, there was a huge snowstorm. The meet was changed, and I was able to compete. After winning Groups, I made it to the Meet of Champions. The Meet of Champions was held on March 1, my birthday. I won the race by a tenth of a second. But the moment prior to crossing the finish, I remember thinking to myself, "*This is it. I have to do it now. I can only do it now.*" And then it was over.

I will never forget that feeling prior to finishing. Life had paused and I had this one chance to control it, but I had to make the move. Winning a state championship was much more rewarding than my experience at Millrose Games. Some may say it was just "luck" that the meet had been moved. For me, it was all part of *His* plan. This race was four years in the making. I didn't increase my mileage, nor did I increase the number of ice baths. I increased my faith and confidence that I was just as capable as anyone else.

Rewind back to my freshman year at Penn, soaking wet, walking through a hailstorm with an F of a grade sticking out of my backpack, I realized how much difference a year makes. I didn't have a birthday cake that year because I was too stressed for the upcoming exam the next day. You may ask, what is the cause for something like that? How can one year be so drastically different from the next?

My answer: The Female Athlete Triad.

I ran all of high school with an inconsistent period. When I told doctors about this at the time, they did not seem to worry. They claimed I was a runner and that it was common. Today, with the increased medical knowledge and literature, this triad is occurring in many female athletes. The female athlete triad can impact physically active women. The three main aspects of the triad include:[19]

1. Low energy availability.[20]
2. Menstrual Dysfunction (Irregular or absent menstrual periods).[21]
3. Low bone mineral density.[22]

There is this disconnect involving active individuals engaging in exercise without fueling themselves properly. For some individuals, low energy may stem from insufficient caloric intake. Athletes do not always see food as energy

19 Siobhan M. Statuta, "The Female Athlete Triad, Relative Energy Deficiency in Sport, and the Male Athlete Triad: The Exploration of Low-Energy Syndromes in Athletes," *Current Sports Medicine Reports* 19, no. 2 (February 2020): 43.

20 Ibid.

21 Ibid.

22 Ibid.

availability. Low energy can also stem from an increase in training and energy expenditure.[23]

From a personal standpoint, I wish I knew this. I wish I was educated on the female athlete triad much sooner, as it was not until freshman year of college that I had even heard this term. I believe had I tackled this early on, and had I been mindful of the impact adequate nutrition had on my body, a majority of my injuries could have been avoided. A majority of my time injured and away from the track could have been prevented.

An orthopedist doctor told me: "The injuries you are having now in college may even be from not regulating your period in high school." I began to appreciate this information and realized young athletes need to be mindful of this. Young athletes need to be cognizant that actions today will impact them in their later years.

I struggled with the female athlete triad throughout college. I had the femoral stress fracture first, followed by a tibial and cuboid stress fracture. Each diagnosis was related to not getting my period and my low bone density due to the lack of estrogen. I felt as if I was trying to make up for lost time, while also trying to train at a high, collegiate level. It was difficult for me because I had earned the opportunity to run in college, and yet, I was hindered from doing so due to my injuries. I was consistently running a fine line between racing on the track and being seated at the doctor's for another examination because of the pain I was feeling.

---

23 Siobhan M. Statuta, "The Female Athlete Triad, Relative Energy Deficiency in Sport, and the Male Athlete Triad: The Exploration of Low-Energy Syndromes in Athletes," *Current Sports Medicine Reports* 19, no. 2 (February 2020): 43.

This was a mental burden.
I was not okay.

I constantly tried to remain altruistic and positive. It was difficult to constantly hear bad news, and it was difficult to constantly get injured. With each bone stress fracture, I had to sit out at least six to eight weeks from running. This is the amount of time it takes for bone to heal. Always cautious, I would extend my recoveries to ten weeks off from running. I had three different stress fractures during my time in college.

Three injuries x ten weeks was a total of thirty weeks I spent cross-training.

Thirty weeks I did not see teammates for our usual regimented practice.

Thirty weeks I had the mental pain that I was doing something wrong.

When individuals come back from injury and finally have the green light to run again, they do so gradually to limit reinjury. When I started running I did so on the AlterG® treadmill. The AlterG® treadmill allows you to run at only a small percentage of your bodyweight. This approach provides the bones with a slow progression for withstanding full body weight when running. The aim is to eventually run at 100 percent body weight.

Once I reached 100 percent of my body weight, I was not able to just start working out with my teammates. I had to gradually incorporate speed workouts so my muscles and bones had time to acclimate to the new intensity. I did not want to get hurt again, so I was slow at coming back. My coach always made sure of this, and I thank him for that.

I would estimate it took at least six to eight weeks until I felt like I was back doing normal runs with normal effort.

Eight weeks of additional caution x three injuries = twenty-four weeks.

Twenty-four weeks + thirty weeks = fifty-four weeks.

Fifty-four weeks is on average thirteen and a half months.

Over a year spent at my four-year collegiate experience where I was not a regulated, regimented athlete arriving to practice each day. Granted, I was very cautious and extended my recovery time to ensure optimal healing. These bone injuries also do not account for the time I took off when I partially tore my plantar fascia in both feet, which followed a similar healing progression.

The time pressure with injuries was said best during an interview with Liz Lansing, who ran at Duke University class of 2019. Her statement said:

"During my injuries, I usually felt devastated. It was hard watching my teammates run off together, while I had to cross-train. It was hard to not want to rush the process, while simultaneously fearing I would get hurt again. The brevity of the four years we had to compete at the collegiate level certainly invoked anxiety that I could not waste any time."

Liz suffered from various injuries, including two stress fractures in the metatarsals of her foot, hamstring tendonitis, and plantar fasciitis. Liz also understands the mental toll injuries have on the athlete, especially when coming back from them.

"The injuries that result from the repetitive, pounding motions of running foster immense distrust of our own bodies that can make it difficult to return to running confidently and not carry any residual mental wounds/scars from the experience."

I personally carried mental wounds. Thirteen and a half months of trying to come back caused me anxiety, mental fatigue, and fear with each step I took toward running again. I had the support during my injuries. I had a devoted coach with whom I am still friends, a dedicated trainer, and the great resources that Penn provided me with. Despite having all this, there was something important that I was missing.

As a neuroscience major in undergrad, and a doctor of physical therapy student now, I can see where in the injury process I struggled—**mental injury**. Mental injury, from my own personal perspective, encompasses the negative thoughts developed during the injury process. I feel mental injury develops 1.) when there is an unawareness of the mental impact injury has on an individual, and 2.) when emotional insecurities about one's injury develop.

I lacked literacy on the psychological component that an injury would have on me. The lost identity I felt, the insecurity of another injury I would eventually feel, and the difficult transition between healthy to injured were all experienced with no warning in sight. I consistently questioned my own emotions and felt insecure about them. At one point I questioned if the thoughts plaguing me were normal, and if I myself were normal.

I feel my own personal mental injury could have been changed had I talked about how I was feeling. I told teammates, friends, and family about my physical injury, but I never spoke about my mental injury. From a checklist standpoint, I did everything I physically could do; I changed my nutrition, went to physical therapy, and even saw an endocrinologist. Yet, I never expressed my true negative emotions.

I was close to having osteoporosis as a nineteen-year-old woman, and this was something that horrified me. I kept this fear bottled inside, and it impacted my mental strength greatly.

One day, I hope athletes will feel they can share their hard stories. This is not just for the athletic world alone, but also society. We see displayed around us individuals talking about their workout, their splits, their upcoming events, but it is rare for individuals to openly talk about eating disorders, physical breakdowns, or mental health. These topics are hidden, but do not let my words alone prove the impact talking about one's mental injury can have.

SIERRA CASTENADA: PRINCETON UNIVERSITY, CLASS OF 2020:

I interviewed Sierra Castenada, who ran at Princeton University. Sierra has suffered her fair share of injuries, including a sacral stress fracture, femoral stress fracture, and a tibial stress reaction. Sierra mentioned how she too struggled with the female athlete triad, and the impact it had on her bone health. When senior year began and her final cross-country season unfolded, she felt motivated and excited for the upcoming season. However, eventually Sierra began to feel an emotion that was all too familiar to her: pain. Sierra was feeling pain in her third metatarsal (toe), but she wanted to keep running since her final Heptagonal Cross-Country Race was coming up.

On race day, the gun went off and Sierra began physically running alongside her teammates. Mentally, however, Sierra was not in the race: "It wasn't until the stress fracture in my foot that I had a breakdown at HEPS. I dropped out of the race. This was the tipping point for me, and I didn't want to keep living like this. I really leaned on teammates a lot during this time and thank goodness for them."

Many years of injury and frustration had consumed Sierra, and she finally felt the weight off her shoulders after talking and sharing her struggles with her teammates. Her hesitancy initially was a worry that she would impact the team culture by sharing this information, despite knowing deep down that wouldn't happen.

Sierra also added that certain topics may not be talked about because most athletes hide their struggles very carefully. From the outside looking in, you may not know the battles they are waging. "Making things okay to talk about is a good team culture," Sierra stated.

Today, Sierra continues to run and explore the vast world of running. Sierra recently went to Colorado to train at altitude. Navigating the terrain in Utah and the rocky ridges in Colorado, she feels strong and capable. In summary, these real-life personal stories are meant to relay the importance of runners engaging in conversations with one another: more specifically, talking about our injuries, the healing process, and the isolation we may feel.

We as healthcare providers, friends, and family also have a role to play. We need to be mindful of mental injury, a framework that can develop when athletes are injured. Talking about the fear, the depressive thoughts, and the frustrations will validate them. Having someone to talk about them with will foster hope for the future. If we work together, our injured friends won't feel insecure about their own emotions. By engaging in the conversation, you become a vital part of a healthy recovery.

I want to transform the running identity into that of a holistic one: a viewpoint that considers the mental and physical health of athletes with a goal for starting the race, and not always on the finish. It is important to understand the existence of mental injury, and a holistic viewpoint can assist in doing just that.

Prior to unveiling the importance of considering the holistic athlete, I must finish *the beginning.* I was diagnosed with the female athlete triad, and I spoke of the difficulty I had with my own mental injury. I cannot move on without shedding light on a specific emotion many injured athletes feel...guilt. Guilt led me to understand the injured psyche of athletes. Guilt allowed me to realize and appreciate seeing the athlete holistically. Before we can move on through this book, we must transcend how we approach guilt, so we can truly accept our injuries as multilayered and not simply physical. Once we do, we can truly open ourselves toward becoming a holistic athlete.

***

Take Away:

- Remember you are not alone.
- Do not be afraid to seek comfort and explain your emotions.
- Normalize hard topics...in time they no longer will feel hard, but rather natural.
- We must all work together to transform the running identity.

Coming Up:

- Understanding the impact *guilt* plays in mental injury.
- How to conquer guilt so we can cultivate a holistic athlete identity.

CHAPTER FOUR A:

GAMBLING WITH GUILT

What if?
What if I didn't run so many miles?
What if I didn't change my sneakers?
What if I took more rest days?
If we feel guilty, are we able to move forward?

I believe guilt is one of the stronger components of mental injury. Again, mental injury is a term I have used to describe the thoughts and the repercussions I accumulated during the injury process. More specifically, my mental injury stemmed from an unawareness of the mental impact I would feel during my injuries and the emotional insecurities I developed.

How our brains perceive ourselves is how we will treat ourselves. Combating and healing these thoughts are part of the injury process.

The question "what if" can plague the mind during injury. A tendency toward pausing life and instead rehashing the past, when running was momentous and easy...when running was attainable. Now, with running paused and the mind still free, we begin to live in the past. When we think about "what if," we are allowing ourselves to go backward, rather than focusing our energy forward.

I was notorious for thinking about the past. There were many days when I would continuously live in the past and try to find exactly when and where I went wrong in my training that led to my injury. I was hoping I could look at my calendar and see, "I ran too many miles on October 2."

This was not the case. I was too focused on the day it happened, and not so much *why* it happened. I thought injuries were a sudden event. While this holds true, injuries can also be gradual, occurring even before the pain is felt. Pain also does not always indicate the onset of an injury, but rather the point at which the body is saying, "I need a break." In school I learned about the physical stress our body feels during both athletic and everyday tasks. The continuous repetitive stress from running accumulates over time when we allow inadequate recovery, something I personally did not take into consideration enough.

My mind never thought about injury in high school. I focused on recovery, but not at the level that was required of a body undergoing so many miles and repetitive stress. It was not until I had my first injury in college that I began to analyze my training and recovery as an influencer to injury.

As I mentioned previously, my first of five injuries in college was my femoral stress fracture during the fall of 2014 due to the female athlete triad—when females lack adequate nutrition to maintain menses. The femur is the largest bone in the body, and yet, mine had a stress fracture. The pain came on gradually. I thought it was just a muscular strain and that some stretching and foam rolling would fix it. I continued to run, and I continued to feel pain. I even decided to run a race thinking I could run through the pain.

Race day came, and with it very cold conditions and cumulus clouds. The air was raw and rainy, and the pressure in the atmosphere made my leg throb even more. I knew then that I had to see a doctor. After I was diagnosed with the stress fracture, the doctor told me, "You will take six to eight weeks off from running, and then we will implement a slow, gradual return to a running program."

SPRING TRACK:

Once I was healed and was back to running that spring, however, I fell into a routine where I felt fearless once again. I felt content because I was back on track doing what I loved. Going to practice at 3:15 p.m. each day was my body's physical way of expending energy and my mind's mental way of rejuvenating. The run provided my mind with perspective and appreciation. After I ran, I found clarity; I felt comforted and at ease.

But anytime I felt pain, I paused...I feared it. Plagued by the doctor's words from my first injury, I reflected on how cautious I was supposed to be coming back from an injury. I immediately started to calculate the miles I ran that week and the amount of food I ate. I was trying to retrace my tracks to figure out if I missed something. I would think about my sleep, and then worry that I did not get enough. Did I do enough to recover after each run?

Anytime pain occurred, my heart would race. From a figurative standpoint, I ran so many steps into the doctor's office only to be told I had to walk out because of a new injury. Walking for me was far more laborious than running. The front desk workers at the health clinic began to tell me, "You should just set up a bed here."

I realized the guilt bubbling inside me was creating even greater pain. The people around me were realizing how fragile I was. I felt guilty. With each of my injuries I consistently felt I had done something wrong. Even when I was healthy, any time I felt pain I immediately was worried I did something wrong; I felt guilty for an injury that did not even exist yet. My mind continuously thought, "This is all my fault." For a while I thought it was only I who felt guilty for my injuries, until I interviewed Julia Trethewey.

Julia Trethewey, a freshman at Georgetown University, also felt the mental burdens that come with being injured. During her 2019 high school junior winter track season, Julia became a New Jersey State Champion in the 3200m race. She continued on into the spring season, breaking records and again moving on to higher, more elite races like Nationals in North Carolina. That summer following her junior year she continued to keep up with her training. She was focused, determined, and excited for her final and last cross-country season in high school. However, Julia never had a chance to lace up for cross-country. Julia instead found herself sidelined during cross-country after having pain in her right hip. "It was a pain I had never felt, and I knew something was wrong," Julia explained.

Patient and hopeful, Julia diverted her attention away from any conclusions until she underwent an MRI. But the runner's blood continued to fill her veins and fill her heart. The waiting game was not easy. After taking a few days off from running, Julia returned to the doctor's office to discuss the MRI. Julia, like me, sat in the doctor's office, waiting and feeling nervous for what the doctor might tell her. Patiently sitting on the edge of the bed while also making small talk with her dad, the minutes turned into miles missed. The doctor entered and told Julia she had a stress reaction in her hip. The hip is a ball-and-socket joint, allowing high mobility. However, when this joint gets injured, it is important to treat and rehab the hip properly and slowly in order to allow continued range of motion and mobility later on.

Julia was given advice from her doctor to take time off from running and start physical therapy once appropriate. With running halted, Julia turned to cross-training to allow herself to keep cardiovascular and aerobic fitness. She tried swimming for the first time. "I really enjoyed cross-training and working various muscles. It made me realize that I want to continue doing it."

But she missed the post-run adrenaline. Working out in isolation for many weeks straight without seeing her teammates created distance from both her team and goals. Julia felt this was all her doing: "When you get injured, you feel guilty in a way. I felt bad."

I believe this particular emotion occurs since injuries happen due to some form of human decision-making. Was the increase in mileage too quick? Or was it the lack of nutrients provided? Was it even the lack of sleep? Personally, I would replay scenarios over and over in my head. I was consumed in the past, rather than focusing on arriving back on the track healthier—that is, until I had a wake-up call one morning.

REPLACING GUILT:

One morning, my coach told me I could do a threshold run with thirty-second pick-ups every three minutes. I was ecstatic, as this was my first taste of speed for some time after rehabilitating my femoral stress fracture. My town has this beautiful trail that is flat, quiet, and perfect for running. I got to the trail early in the morning when the dew was still nestled softly on the ground and the fog was slowly clearing away. I completed a warm-up and then began my first thirty-second threshold. It felt wonderful to go a little faster for once.

After I finished that set, however, my mind defaulted back to the idea, "What if I get injured?"

My mind mentally began feeling guilty for something that had not even happened yet.

I was running my first workout since my injury, and yet immediately my mind returned to the past...back toward the fear. My mind was associating speed with injury, and not courage, excitement, a strong being...but rather a weak one. We cannot let the injuries impact our current, present, precious day we have been granted. Julia concluded the injury experience best: "A moment of my life. I got injured, it happened. You don't run for eight weeks and it will be okay. You have your whole life." Julia reframed her outlook on the injury. She stated, "You can adapt."

The best way to truly adapt is finding the origin of the injury. Focusing our efforts forward involves considering one's previous training with honest reflection. The times in which I lived in the past were also the times when I was not being honest with myself, as I tried to ignore the truth. I did not want to admit to the fact that I failed to nourish my body appropriately and that I ran too many miles too fast.

If you do not adapt to the situation and find the origin, you are hindering the opportunity to return to your sport with increased knowledge. What greater power is there than knowledge and self-care for yourself? However, I know this is difficult. This is not something that can happen overnight, and it is common for the guilt to manifest itself back into one's heart.

But what if we replace Guilt with Grit. Angela Lee Duckworth, author of *Grit: The Power of Passion and Perseverance*, explains this concept of Grit in her book. She also spoke at a TED Talk on what grit means. She stated,

"Grit is passion and perseverance for very long-term goals. Grit is having stamina. Grit is sticking with your future, day in, day out, not just for the week, not just for the month, but for years..."[24]

There is pride in not feeling guilty when thinking about the origins of your injury, because you are channeling grit. Grit is using this new knowledge you discovered about yourself, your training, and your mental strength to design a plan for a healthy life.

Prior to stepping back on the track or field, you must feel full of new knowledge about yourself. You must be filled with Grit and no Guilt. Angela ended the TED Talk by saying, "... We have to be willing to fail, to be wrong, to start over again with lessons learned."[25]

Well, was I? Are you?

---

24 Angela L. Duckworth, "Grit: The Power of Passion and Perseverance," filmed April 2013 at TED conference, TED video, 6:01.

25 Ibid.

CHAPTER FOUR B:

APPLYING THE GRIT

At first, I wasn't ready to start over. I came back from my injury struggling during workouts that were once easy. One practice in particular consisted of 200-meter repeats. After only four repeats, I was leaning against the wall of Franklin Field and gasping for air, my legs throbbing for oxygen. A friend on the team came over to me and said, "It will get easier, just give it time."

I knew it would, and I molded an attitude that each accomplished workout would lead me closer to a big meet. I remained gritty, and I was not focusing on running alone. I considered other components of training that were involved in maintaining good health, including my nutrition and recovery. After practice, I went to the dining hall and did not just eat dinner, but also made snacks including yogurt parfaits, peanut butter sandwiches, and any other adequate fuel source. I needed protein because my body was still recovering from the earlier strenuous workout.

I continued to be cautious with my mileage, too, and my coach and I created a plan that focused more on quality and not on volume. My training consisted of running the long run on Sunday with the team and two to three workouts a week. In total, I was running four to five times a week in college. I never ran any doubles, and I never second-guessed my training with my coach, yet I second-guessed my own efforts and potential—that is, until I had the opportunity to "race."

I ran my first 5,000-meter track race ever at Widener University—a small school, but a big moment for me as I never envisioned myself as more than a 1,500-meter runner. To this day I can clearly remember that track meet.

WIDENER UNIVERSITY: 5,000-METER RACE

"Are you nervous?" my teammate asked. "Surprisingly, I'm not nervous, more so excited," I responded, while sitting patiently in the stands awaiting the start of my race. I told myself this race was a challenge; I just had to go out and hold on. My lack of nervousness was also because I put no pressure on myself. I had come back from a difficult injury, and I made efforts to ensure the small details were accounted for. At this point in my life, making it to a meet *was* my success, as I had this opportunity to actually race.

Sitting in the bleachers, eating my usual peanut butter and banana sandwich, I felt content just being at the meet. I saw one of my high school teammates and was reminded of my past running days in high school. The 5,000-meter race was the last event, and we were finally given the okay to begin our warm-up: a fifteen-minute light shakeout followed by some dynamic drills and strides.

The sun was slowly beginning its decent when it was time to toe the line. I felt so relaxed and so present in the blanket of warmth from the sun.

The gun went off, the race began, and I kept expecting myself to feel tired, but it never happened. Instead, toward the end I felt really good and trusted myself. I won the race and ran a 16:40 5k that day. While the run was great, what made me most excited was just racing. I returned to my sport, and not just the run. I had remained gritty and combated my guilt.

The key emotion of this race was confidence. I felt strong and I was not worried about my injuries or the potential of becoming injured again. I had prepared for the race, from both a nutritional and training standpoint. I had prepared so deliberately to make it to the start line; now all I had to do was race. I deserved to race, as I remained motivated.

2016 PENN RELAYS

This same motivated, gritty feeling carried with me to the Penn Relays. The Penn Relays takes place in Franklin Field at the University of Pennsylvania. This historic track meet brings a diverse group of athletes together, from professional runners to high school athletes. I personally feel that there is always some kind of magic in the air during the relays.

During the relays there is "distance night," which is when the longer college distance races occur, including the 10K, 5K, and 3K races. I was registered to participate in the 5K. The evening of the 2016 Penn Relays distance night included freezing cold rain that delayed the start of many races. There were so many details out of my control that I decided my sole focus would be arriving to the race when it was called.

There was a darkened sky by the time we were called to the line, and the temperature was so cold that snowflakes began to fall. Despite the cold weather, the adrenaline and excitement during the race left me feeling full of pride for my team. I felt the same relaxation as I did at Widener Field. The last eight hundred meters of the race, my coach yelled to me, "Kylene, trust yourself." I broke from the pack and ran my best 5K that night. Later that spring, I found out that race time qualified me to the NCAA Regionals in Jacksonville, Florida. This was the furthest I ever made it as a collegiate athlete; all because of one race and remaining gritty.

MARGARET THOMSON: BUCKNELL UNIVERSITY, CLASS OF 2019

My story aside, other runners have reaped the benefits of remaining gritty. Margaret Thomson, a runner from Bucknell University, lived by the motto "Details matter." After interviewing Margaret, I grew a strong appreciation for how gritty she remained during times of injury.

As a distance runner, Margaret enjoyed running races from the mile to the 5K. She was also a very cautious runner, especially in regard to her mileage, and would incorporate cross-training in order to maintain a healthy number of miles.

The August prior to her junior year cross-country season, however, Margaret started feeling right Achilles pain the week prior to her team training camp. The Achilles tendon is what connects your calf muscles to the back of your heel bone. Margaret attempted to run during camp, but the pain was too unbearable.

The biggest frustration for her was having this injury despite always taking care of the details. She was big on ensuring she recovered properly, and she also completed weightlifting exercises, all to confirm she was healthy and training strong. "I started freaking out about the injury and was afraid I would be really slow when I came back."

During her time off from running, she used a lot of passive modalities on the injury spot, including massage, ultrasound, and ice. She also enjoyed cross-training and began to incorporate more hip strengthening. However, her injury did not follow any set timeline and she was not provided a designated date for when she could return to running. This was frustrating since she had to take the injury day by day.

Despite the long hiatus from running, Margaret was able to come back and run in the 2017 League Cross-Country Championship. This energy was subdued, however, by a tightening pain in her calf. Her injury returned during that following winter track season: "I had gone for a ten-mile progression run with the front pack of the team, and the next day my Achilles tendon acted up again."

The rest of her winter season was spent sidelined. During her injury, she too struggled with the burden of mental injury and feeling distant from the team. Despite the frustration of this ongoing injury, Margaret continued to appreciate the details. All winter season, Margaret focused her efforts on cross-training, completing her physical therapy exercises, and enjoying a mental break from running. When the spring season came, she was still a very strong athlete despite not having a lot of mileage.

That spring, Margaret was put in the 2018 Championship League Meet and came in fourth place after hardly running! This same momentum followed her as she qualified for a race at ECAC and had one of the best races of her collegiate career: *"People came up to me after my race and were really cheering me on! In that moment all the time away was well worth it. I put in the work and it really paid off. A huge part of it was also trusting that what I was doing was okay!"*

I appreciate Margaret's story as she demonstrated how valuable it is to remain gritty. When her injury came back, Margaret decided she would continue to live by "details matter," even though she was injured. Details do matter, and sometimes the results occur much later on than we might wish them to. Even though she did not have many miles, her body was still strong when she came back—strong in a new, profound way.

Margaret's story also exemplifies how the best athlete out there is not the one with the most mileage. During her injury, Margaret exercised and used different muscles with her cross-training. Her body was allowed a break from the repetitive aspects of running and was instead challenged in a different way.

In summary, never feel guilty for passion. Passion can lead to injury if we become narrow-minded, but passion is also beautiful. Hearing someone talk about their passions gives me appreciation for their story. Always appreciate your passions, but when you are halted from them, feel gritty! You will find that stepping away from familiarity will grant you knowledge, trust, and grit. Feeling guilty is one of the mental injuries that runners feel, but do not be hard on yourself for this. Remind yourself to channel this guilt into *grit*. And so, again I ask,

Are you "willing to fail, to be wrong, to start over again with lessons learned?"[26]

***

Take Away:

- Forgive the guilt in your heart.
- Then remove the guilt in your heart.
- Finally, allow grit to fill your heart instead.

---

26 Angela L. Duckworth, "Grit: The Power of Passion and Perseverance," filmed April 2013 at TED conference, TED video, 6:01.

Coming Up:

- The gritty athlete is also a holistic one.

CHAPTER FIVE:

HEALING WORDS

I did it. I replaced guilt with grit, and I was back on the track. But I did not remain there. I broke again...and again. Despite understanding mental injury, and replacing guilt with grit, there was something I was missing. This is the chapter I lived that led me to realize this book needed to be written. I focused on the mental component of injury, but it was this personal story of mine that led me to understand the importance of cultivating a holistic identity. The end of the beginning; the race still unfinished.

FALL 2016 CROSS-COUNTRY SEASON

When can I come back?

I learned how to read physicians' faces after asking this question. When they smiled, they were hopeful. When they started documenting notes in my chart, they were uncertain. I consistently saw injury as a timeline, focusing on the end date—when I could run again. I was persistent and motivated, yet I failed to consider components of healing apart from the day I could run again.

What kind of training timeline stopped injuries from persistently occurring...and how could I attain it? I found my answer after my third and fourth injuries—**the battle of plantar fasciitis.**

The start of my 2016 cross-country season started off on the wrong foot, especially when that foot has plantar fasciitis. From my background in physical therapy school, simplified terminology for this diagnosis is heel pain.

I struggled all of cross-country with this diagnosis: a constant pounding at the bottom of my foot...a headache that never went away. I did everything I could to alleviate the pain, but it never decreased. I stretched, used a tennis ball on the bottom of my foot to massage the area, and even went to physical therapy for treatment. I started to dread practice because of the pain I felt. *I began to hate the run, but still loved the race.*

Later in the season I was granted an opportunity to travel with the team to Madison, Wisconsin, for a race. I was ecstatic. I had very fast, talented teammates, and racing with them granted me appreciation and excitement for the sport. On the day prior to the race, the team and I visited the course in order to familiarize ourselves with the terrain. Madison is a beautiful sight to see in the fall, and I was enjoying not only the sights but also the chance to spend time with my teammates. The best part too was that my foot felt great, and I had very little pain.

The next morning, however, a different reality struck. On the day of a race, it is custom to run a fifteen-minute shake-out run before leaving for the course. My foot was in such pain that I skipped the shake-out. As a runner, I lived with the saying "mind over matter." I told myself to suck it up and that my pre-race adrenaline would mask the pain.

At the starting line, one of my favorite songs began to play. I was so caught up in the moment and my pre-race adrenaline that I forgot about my foot.

The gun went off, signaling the start of the race. My adrenaline lasted a total of five seconds when I felt a sharp, painful snap in the bottom of my foot. I thought my foot split in half. I kept racing because I was a "runner." I was hoping the cheers would propel me to the finish, but the pain on my face indicated otherwise. I was approaching the hill when my coach told me to step off. I hesitated for only half a second, because deep down I was so thankful she did. I had never not finished a race, and stepping off the course that day also meant stepping toward months of recovery and injury...yet again.

I fell to the ground once off the course, as I couldn't put weight on my foot without excruciating pain. I was picked up by the father of one of my teammates and was carried into the medical tent. An evaluation of my foot soon unfolded; "Does this hurt?" "Can you move your toes?" "How much pain do you feel when I press here?" I answered their questions, and they responded by handing me a boot to wear. I was told my running days were over before my sweat and tears even had time to dry. I went from being a Division I runner to an injured one within minutes.

I heard the cheers from outside the tent.
I watched other runners come in
with injuries.
The boot on my foot was the last thing I saw
before tears clouded my vision.

"I am in a boot," I told my parents, as I stood meters apart from where other athletes were racing their best times. In my heart I knew I was back in Penn's pool. Leaving the meet, we drove through the beautiful open land in Madison, Wisconsin. I sat by the window trying to hold back my tears; I wanted to make it appear that everything was okay. That perhaps I wasn't really injured again.

At the airport, my coach called me over and told me everything would be alright. She knew I was hurting, and her charismatic words gave me hope and light for this moment. Back at school I had imaging done of my foot, and the results revealed a partially torn plantar fascia. I wore the boot for a while, and I once again missed my favorite season, winter track. I began physical therapy *again*, and I began vigorous cross-training *again.* Eager to get back, eager to follow the "come back" phrase that everyone said to me.

The day I could finally try running was great, as I had no pain in the foot I tore. **However, my other foot still hurt. This foot was the origin to my plantar pain in the beginning.** The foot that had plantar fasciitis pain all summer and all cross-country season was not the one that tore. In the back of my mind, I knew the plantar fasciitis game was **not over yet.** I tore the foot that hadn't hurt in the first place. And so, when I began running again, that same original painful foot kept stabbing me from the ground up.

2017 SPRING TRACK

Despite still feeling strong, persistent pain, I looked forward to training with the team once again. I continued my physical therapy and passive modalities to try and reduce the pain. Later on in the season my coach asked if I wanted to be part of the 4 x Mile at Penn Relays. The 4 x Mile is a relay race involving four teammates, each running a mile and then handing off the baton to their teammate. I cannot even explain my excitement and gratitude for how I felt in that moment.

Stepping onto Franklin Field the Saturday of the Penn Relays was what I believe the quarterback of the Super Bowl feels before the game. I looked around me and saw faces, watched their mouths move, yet did not hear anything at all. Thousands of people were crowded in the stands, colors so vibrant and beautiful were ablaze, and I heard silence. I looked to my left and my right, feeling frozen and untouched in the center of this huge arena. There were athletes on the infield warming up, pole-vaulters soaring through the air, long-jumpers defying seconds of gravity, yet I was at a standstill—basked and immersed in this full-fledged state of amazement.

This was the world of track and field.

When I was handed the baton, I was ready. I had been ready since the gun sounded the start of the 4 x Mile. I was so focused and determined to finish strong for my team. The crowd was full of so much life, the stadium was echoing sounds that all of Philadelphia could hear, and I was the focus. I was the individual in the midst of it all running my heart to the finish.

And then I felt it. With one more lap to go, I felt the familiar pain: the one that represented the tearing of my foot in half. The pain that started from the bottom of my foot yet spread so vast and seeped so deep **that even my mind was tired of the pain.** I had to finish, and I completed the last lap knowing it would be my final one for a while. Never had

I felt so thankful to see the finish line ahead. Afterwards I fell into someone's arms. While they thought it was due to exhaustion, I knew it was because my foot tore.

What made the pain forgettable in that moment was having my three teammates around me to celebrate the race. We broke the 4 x Mile school record that day. After the race I knew I wouldn't be able to go for a cool-down, so I just asked my coach if I could bike. I went to dinner that night, but it was hard to celebrate when I knew deep down the run was over. After leaving my parents, I struggled back to my dorm totally absorbed, once again, by concern for my foot. I tried soaking and rubbing the painful area, telling myself it was all in my head. I even rolled it again with a golf ball.

The next morning, I was unable to stand on my foot. I crawled to the bathroom and then called my coach, telling her I was going to take a taxi to the trainer's office. Driving down Walnut Street to the sound of fans screaming from inside Franklin Field made me feel sad and misplaced, like I was a stranger to the relays.

I felt deja vu when entering the training room and undergoing my evaluation: "Does this hurt?" "Can you move your toes?" "How much pain do you feel when I press here?" Mentally, I was back in Wisconsin, watching as yet again a boot was put onto one of my feet.

The tears came slowly this time, as if my mind and body were both harmoniously processing the fact that I was injured again. Once again, the hours in the pool, of physical therapy, and the very few miles I ran were covered with a familiar nemesis—the black boot.

I tried to hide my tears when I left the office and decided to sit on a statue outside of the chemistry building on Penn's campus. From behind me, the crowd inside the stadium was roaring with excitement, as the announcer stated the new lead runner's name. I sat there for a long time listening but incapable of watching.

Hundreds of strangers surrounded me as I succumbed to my suppressed emotions. I sat on the hard cement statue, allowing the immovable object to anchor me. I tried to erase my rapid heartbeat and flushed skin and face. Runners kept soaring by, and I kept looking down at the box on my foot. The weather was warm, but I felt cold and frozen. Slowly my tears evaporated, leaving small droplets on the statue I was sitting beneath. A few students sauntered by, a few runners gathered and moved on, and I remained alone.

I felt both vulnerable and isolated. Pulling out my cell phone, I called my dad. He was miles away, yet I could feel the pain in his voice saying, "It will be alright." But even his words were just ghostly whispers. I hung up and collapsed in despair. **I was frustrated because how resilient can one be when there is never any safe landing on a hill you keep climbing?**

I no longer kept my head low because I no longer cared; I was entering a gracious place of healing, allowing my body to fully recover without thinking about what I had to do next. I was tired of pretending I was okay, when in reality I was mentally and physically in pieces.

Then I saw her. Through blurred tears and my running mascara I saw a woman walk by, noticing her because of her distinct vibrant, yellow outfit, a resemblance of sunlight and warmth. She stopped walking, turned around, and addressed me. What she said to me changed my life.

"God sent me back to you to tell you that everything will be alright."

I looked up at her. She repeated, **"He told me to come back. He told me to tell you it will be alright."** I let what she said sink in. A true messenger of God himself. A sign, a love letter in words.

I suddenly felt awoken. I realized something had to change; I had to change. Here I was, a passionate athlete, injured and alone once again. This woman told me she was sent to me; my prayers for clarity were answered.

I left that statue with a decision made: I was going to invest in myself and create my own timeline. A timeline that involved changes I wish I had made during the injury process. **A story that could be told and be shared one day to athletes like me.**

I tell this story because at the time, I was seen as one of the faster runners. I was running in an Ivy League uniform, on a Division I team, in a historical area, on the day of the renowned Penn Relays. I had a fast time, and my team had broken the 4 x Mile school record at that time. Stepping off that track that day, however, I was actually the slowest and weakest. I was stepping toward months and months away from the sport.

Months and months back in the pool, walking around with a boot on my foot.

Months and months of doctors' offices and physical therapy treatments.

Months and months away from the bolded calendar date for when I could run again.

***

Take Away:

- Mile times do not indicate the best runner. To be a strong runner you must prepare for the race appropriately. After an injury one's focus should not be on the date they return, but the value of each day during injury. A timeline where each day's attention is on, "How can I arrive physically and mentally stronger this time?"
- You cannot win any race you fail to show up for. To heal an injury is to approach it graciously. Love it, nurture it, and learn from it. Individuals want to read a list of suggestions on how to become the best runner. Truthfully, **the start of the run begins when we understand the holistic athlete. Once you understand that, you are already on the starting line.**

Coming Up:

- What it means to be a holistic athlete.
- The discoveries I made from my previous injury timelines, and what I would have done differently.

PART TWO:

A HOLISTIC IDENTITY

These next subsequent chapters include how to conquer the injury process. These chapters ensure individuals learn what being a holistic athlete encompasses. Included in them are reflections I discovered when looking back on my injury timelines, and how to overcome the injury process through proper mind and body viewpoints. These chapters continue to include stories from other runners and athletes. I hope these stories demonstrate how to physically and mentally heal during the injury process.

CHAPTER SIX:

OBSESSIVE PASSION AND IDENTITY

To be a holistic athlete means to accept and see yourself as not normal.

The beginning of this book outlined the mental injury and distress I endured during my physical injuries. The second part to this book explores where in my running career I went wrong, and what I would have done differently. In addition, interviews from other runners will provide further insight about how to best withstand the injury process.

***

Normalize. Normally. Normal. Norm. No. There is no normal runner. There is no normal success story. After my stress fractures, and my battle with plantar fasciitis, I began to reflect on my choices and how I failed to approach myself and my training from a holistic viewpoint. My first key reflection from my past injury timelines: ***I was an obsessive runner.***

There were a few moments in particular when I became very obsessed with running. One memory specifically stems from the summer of 2015 prior to my sophomore year at Penn. I had been injured the previous winter with my femoral stress fracture but was coming off a strong spring season. I was amped that summer to continue my successful training. However, with high ambitions came along a small, narrowed focus. I was consumed with an obsession for running, leading me eventually toward another injury.

SUMMER 2015:

"I will be back by 9:00 a.m.," I told my mom as I grabbed the keys to our family Dodge Nitro. I was heading to the trail in my town for a tempo run my team had planned. The air was cool and there was a soft, misty fog when I arrived.

I began the run and felt empowered by it: limitless, weightless, and oh so fearless. I was dropping time fast; I felt free. After I finished the run and was stretching, I had this heavy feeling in my heart that injury was coming. The run felt too easy, too undeserved. Was I really training hard enough?

There are many runs like this that are well deserved. I knew from my training that summer that I had taken the easy way out. I avoided every other aspect of training, including my nutrition, my recovery, and my mental health check-ins. I was too focused on numbers: split times and miles run. I had finished a great workout on paper, but how strong was I from a health standpoint?

I came home from the run and sat at the kitchen table. "How was your workout?" my mom asked. "It was good. I hit all the mile splits I wanted," I replied as I began cooking some eggs on the stove. "That is great! Are you working at the market today?" And there was my reminder of a time that summer I had become too obsessed with running.

I thought I was training hard by going on double runs during my break at work. I would run one and half miles during my break, come back, and then stand the rest of my shift. Where was the recovery? That one-and-a-half-mile run actually regressed my training because I had failed to recover after the run.

My mind was focused on only the race, and this prevented it from seeing the unintentional harm I was doing to my body. **Why was I so narrow-minded and obsessed with running?**

I wanted to be the best runner, and this was how I thought the best trained. I thought the best lived and breathed only running, and I thought they ran consistent fast miles every run. I did not realize the best runner monitors their *efforts, not split times.* I would give 100 percent, but my mind was trained to only read numbers on a watch and splits on a clock. These numbers determined my perceived effort and success.

That summer I was supposed to be improving my bone density, which required I allow my body to grow and manifest into the wholesome figure it was meant to be. It was not. I unconsciously ignored the nutritional needs of my body, and I ignored my life outside of running. Where was my nineteen-year-old self? Where were the aspects of myself that involved growing up? What were my other passions and desires apart from running? How was I growing if I only planted the same seed over and over again?

WHAT DOES IT MEAN TO TRULY TRAIN HARD?

Training hard means I am enjoying the run, while tracking how my body physically and mentally feels. It means I am checking in with myself, totally aware that my every move on any day does not have to involve running. That summer, I was not training hard. I was instead focused on the pace of the miles I ran and on eating only healthy foods. I was not acting like a nineteen-year-old enjoying ice cream. I believed ice cream would be a detriment to my running success. This is not training hard, because great training allows oneself to enjoy life, while also lacing up sneakers in the process. Be healthy but be mindful that you can enjoy food you love without feeling as if you are doing your next run a disservice.

THE END OF SUMMER 2015:

"Mom...I have another stress fracture."

LOOKING BACK:

I used to look back on that summer and feel sad, wishing someone had given me a crystal ball to see the negative impact I was inflicting on my body. Today, I am glad I never saw that crystal ball. If I did, I would never have empathy for individuals with pain, with perseverance, and for those with a passionate love for something that continuously falls out of reach. I learned that by trying to become the word, the image, the definition of "runner," I deprived my body unintentionally of the one thing that gave me life: energy.

I was not energizing my body.

And I was not energizing an identity apart from the runner.

THE INJURY:

My obsession with running continued during my injury. I watched people walk around me and wondered if they ever felt the pain I was experiencing. By asking myself, "Do they have strong bones?" I was allowing my mind to focus on what I did not have.

During my injury, the passion and loss of control I felt to run again demonstrated how much my life revolved around it. I found an article that looked into how passion is woven into injuries and recovery. A study completed by Jonge, Balk, and Taris titled "Mental Recovery and Running-Related Injuries in Recreational Runners: The Moderating Role of Passion for Running," consisted of a sample of 246 Dutch recreational runners. These researchers observed mental recovery and the role of passion in relation to running injuries.[27]

- Harmonious passion was stated as the runner having control over running and being able to participate in other activities.[28]
- Obsessive passion consumed the individual, both in their mind and need to run. The runner ultimately loses control over the activity and develops conflict with other activities aside from running. [29]

---

27 Jan de Jonge, Yannick A. Balk, and Toon W. Taris, "Mental Recovery and Running-Related Injuries in Recreational Runners: The Moderating Role of Passion for Running," *International Journal of Environmental Research and Public Health* 17, no. 3 (February 2020): 1-3, 1044.

28 Jan de Jonge, Yannick A. Balk, and Toon W. Taris, "Mental Recovery and Running-Related Injuries in Recreational Runners: The Moderating Role of Passion for Running," *International Journal of Environmental Research and Public Health* 17, no. 3 (February 2020): 5, 1044.

29 Jan de Jonge, Yannick A. Balk, and Toon W. Taris, "Mental Recovery and Running-Related Injuries in Recreational Runners: The Moderating Role of Passion for Running," *International Journal of Environmental Research and Public Health* 17, no. 3 (February 2020): 5, 1044.

I held an obsessive passion. Running was my identity, and when I lost it from injury, I was desirous for some form of control. The only aspect of myself that I knew was the runner and so the control I felt to get it back was all-consuming. A sport is profoundly beautiful and motivating so long as it remains a sport, without infringing on one's health and identity. To see outside of optimal—outside of one narrow, addictive mindset—is to live. At the time, I was obsessive and addicted to a sport. I lost myself because of this and I did not seek alternative aspects of life that I could potentially connect with.

DANA KLEIN: YALE UNIVERSITY, CLASS OF 2018

I was not alone in feeling a lost identity with injury onset. I interviewed Dana Klein, a runner from the Yale University class of 2018, who absolutely loves the sport of running. In high school she was a New Jersey State Champion the winter of 2014 in the 3,200-meter race. Carrying her athletic career with her, she attended Yale University, where she continued to train and challenge her body at a new level. During a time of injury, Dana was removed from familiarity and instead approached recovery with a lost identity.

The physicians were initially uncertain as to the origin of her pain. With extreme pain in both her hips, it was hypothesized Dana had hip impingement, or pain from the labrum surrounding the hip socket. After contemplating surgery, Dana decided she would take a month off from running and allow the inflammation in her hips to diminish. During this month, this self-imposed hiatus from her familiar routine, Dana felt a lack of control and a separation from her identity—both physically and mentally.

"I was definitely feeling self-conscious about my body and I was feeling really far away from the team and my goals that I had going into junior year. All of a sudden they were slipping away." One February morning in particular Dana was headed to the pool, feeling the mental weight of injury and the lack of motivation to swim. "I talked to my mom the whole walk to the pool. I stayed on the phone with her until I had to go jump in the water."

When Dana finally got off the phone and entered the pool, she felt the same emotions that many injured athletes feel—tired and alone. "I jumped into the pool, and then started crying. I did one lap. I couldn't do it and got out." If we could optimize our situations, we would be running with the team. Instead, we are left cross-training alone, afraid, and anxiously waiting to get back.

I asked Dana how she combated this lost identity, and if she did anything to alter her focus. Dana explained how she turned her focus toward her job at school as a communication and consent educator in the office of gender and campus culture. During this experience, she was utilizing her time and efforts towards others and something other than running, including overcoming social norms. This helped distract her mind from her injury. She also decided to book a trip.

"I made a plan and booked a trip to Boulder, Colorado. I told myself I hope that I am healthy by the time that we are there, but even if not, I am going to enjoy myself."

Toward the end of the conversation, I asked Dana if her perception of the injury process changed once she was healthy. Personally, it was difficult to envision my life in the pool once I was back on the track. In retrospect, I was masking the pain I once felt. Dana responded by stating: "I look back on my injury, and how was I feeling that down?"

After five different injuries in college, I will always remember the feelings I encountered. I had to combat physical and mental pain because of something I loved so much. I lived many days wishing I could control my injury and heal my bone myself. Pondering my personal experiences, I thought about what Dana said. Dana reflected on the injury process in general, saying:

"Did the experience need to be as negative as it was for me to grow, or is there a way young collegiate distance runners who get injured can step away and see this time as more of a process than something negative?"

Dana is right: how can we alter the injury process so it is not something so negative?

My answer—through the creation of an optimal mindset. This mindset will allow one's identity to branch away from an obsessive need for running. I can be Kylene, *a* runner; not *the* runner.

***

Coming Up:

- Cultivating a new mindset.
- The invention of an identity apart from miles run.

CHAPTER SEVEN

A NEW MINDSET

Holistic athletes think optimally, despite not always living it.

How do we truly adapt to a situation that is far from optimal?

How do we settle for less than what we want?

How do we not ask ourselves, "What if?"

I believe there is no such event as an optimal situation.

What does exist is a mindset leading us to believe something is optimal. Too many minutes of our lives are spent planning and trying to ensure optimal can happen. We busy ourselves with calendars and deadlines in hopes the goal we have in mind will be reached. Life has its own course of events that is both unpredictable and uncontrollable.

My obsessive passion for running was altered once I found myself outside of my *normal* environment and my *normal* routine. At the time, I had finally received the green light from the doctor that I could run on an AlterG® treadmill. Penn did not have one on campus, so I had to take the bus into Center City, Philadelphia, to run in a physical therapy clinic that did have one. It was during this experience that my new mindset was cultivated.

AN IMPORTANT, EYE-OPENING EXPERIENCE:

Growing up in a small town, I was not used to public transportation. I was rehabilitating my femoral stress fracture and was told to come back slowly by running only a percentage of my body weight for a few weeks. The AlterG® treadmill provided me this opportunity and allowed my bones and muscles to adapt to the stress of running again without full body weight.

It took some trial and error and missed bus times before I finally reconciled down the bus schedule. I eventually adapted to city transportation and waited every day at the same bus stop at 3:15 p.m. to ride into Center City. At times, standing at that bus stop made me sad. While the rest of my team was gearing up for a challenging workout, I was standing in the cold. With the snow slowly seeping into my hair, and my eyes squinting to see under heavy eyelids, I began to feel sorry for myself.

After my physical therapy appointment, I rode the bus back toward campus. City transportation is definitely a melting pot of various individuals. I remember on one day in particular a woman sitting across from me had an older woman's face on a small child's body. A young child walked onto the bus with her mom, stopped, stared at the woman, and pointed at her, saying, "Ew."

I ran off at the next bus stop with tears streaming down my face. I was supposed to meet friends for dinner, but I was too devastated for that. I was hurt by the way society failed to see the beautiful light and life within each being. No matter what society sees as wrong or different, I know there is a soul in each body with this powerful potential to touch the world, despite their unawareness. To see someone as unique, diverse, and full of life is beautiful. Kindness is beautiful. Love is beautiful. Energy is beautiful.

The rest of that night I would revisit the scene I saw and grow sad and weary. It was the first time in a while my mind was preoccupied with something other than myself or running. I was awoken after that bus scene. I had to see more to life, and I needed to remind myself of the vast world outside of a circular dimension. It took physically and mentally removing myself from my normal life to do so, but it was eye opening to realize how far removed I became from the real life; the one outside my "bubble."

I realized how far I had come from appreciating and being grateful for the beauty within life. I turned my eye to just how beautiful life could be, which required that I craft a mindset to see the beauty. Despite life not being optimal, I should have shaped a mindset to see optimal.

Perhaps this altered mindset could have impacted my view on my own injuries. Instead, I would have seen going to physical therapy as something positive, taking necessary steps to come back as a healthier runner. At the time, I did not see riding the bus to physical therapy as a victory, a step toward recovering, but an affront to my desperate need of returning to running, as this was not the normal. This was not what I saw on Instagram or on runner profiles. I did not see running websites talking about an injured athlete waiting for the bus to run on a treadmill. This was not the *norm.*

THE NEXT DAY:

I went to the pool the next morning with extremely low motivation. I was still reflecting on what I internalized from the bus, and my heart and motivation were not aligned. When I got to the pool, however, I noticed another individual aqua jogging. I asked if she wanted to aqua jog together, and soon learned her name was Jen. She mentioned using cross-training as a means to recover and overcome injuries. She was going through similar struggles from injury, so we decided we would try and meet up different mornings to aqua jog together. She was on the club track for Drexel but often ran on her own.

JEN MULLER:

Jen is a very intelligent woman: she has a B.S. in biomedical engineering, an M.S. in biochemical engineering, and is working toward her PhD in bioengineering.

I recently had the opportunity to catch up with Jen. After posting about my book idea on Instagram, Jen reached out to me. Once I interviewed her, I learned the greater depth of her story and her injuries. What I really appreciated was Jen's knowledge and awareness of her own identity and energy. She tended to her health from various viewpoints: from a self-love standpoint and from a nutritional standpoint.

These practices, however, did not happen overnight. Jen stated that she had reflected on her past and the actions that led to injuries, explaining, *"I wouldn't have run through everything. I would have eased up on cross-training, and I would have been easier on myself. I think I would have tried to be less scared. A lot of the times I was so scared of getting injured that I would drive myself into another injury."*

Since her injuries, Jen has made some of her own changes. Waking up at 5:20 a.m. each morning, Jen still will head out on a run. She finds starting her day with exercise sets the tone for the rest of the day as she is doing something for herself prior to accomplishing anything work-related. When she can't run, though, she is easy on herself and engages in other interests. She still wakes up at 5:20 a.m. on these days because this is her self-care time. Instead of putting on her sneakers to hit the Philadelphia streets, she grabs her pencil and begins to draw. The first thing she does in the morning is care for herself.

When Jen told me this, I realized the value in designating a few minutes of my day to just myself. We prioritize time toward our work, toward our family, our friends, but what do we do each day for ourselves? For some individuals this means working out. But when you can't get in a workout or when you have a rest day, perhaps you could devote time to another passion? Perhaps the injury would no longer be crippling you but rather allowing you to spread your wings. How powerful is this? This moment, this finite instance to extend your identity into your own unknown potentials.

This is not easy, and I know how busy and how hard individuals work. When I had a very busy graduate school schedule, I challenged myself with this task. At night, I began to pray more. It took a few minutes, but I found such contentment with praying. Praying allowed me to confront my most paralyzing worry and let go of it. I never felt alone when I prayed, either. Those dedicated moments at the end of the day were mine, and they gave me a sense of ownership and gratitude. I know praying may not be the answer for everyone, but even just writing something down before going to sleep can be uplifting. Any task that provides self-care time for you is important and is not emphasized enough. To be mentally happy, you need to designate time for yourself.

Aside from designated time for herself, Jen also keeps herself in check. Working out for Jen is important for her mind, and so, in order to allow herself to work out and enjoy it, she schedules time with a nutritionist. She does not go weekly, but rather on occasion when perhaps her workouts and training have changed and she wants to ensure she is keeping up with her metabolic demand.

As the conversation progressed, we circled back to our own personal reflections of our injuries. Apart from my own personal advice I have for runners and athletes, I wanted to hear from Jen's perspective. "If you could give advice to an individual, what would it be?" Jen responded,

"You physically need to learn how to listen to your intuition. Trust yourself. Be easy on yourself."

Being easy on yourself. Something easily said, hard to do.

How do we do this when we see success all around us on social media? I personally had to work on this. I began to reflect on my experience on the Philly bus when I hurried off in tears. I was unable to see through the tears, and yet, never in my life had I felt such clarity. It was clear to me: to be easy on ourselves we need to accept ourselves as different. We need to open our minds. We need to remind ourselves of how small we are in comparison to this whole world.

I was different. My story is different. But I am not alone. I was on the bus that day with over twenty other individuals. Was their big concern when they were going to run again or how many miles they ran that day? When I was a senior in high school my English teacher, Ms. Gonzalez, provided me advice that I failed to appreciate until I stepped off the bus that day. She told me,

"You need to step into a room with the idea that someone holds a burden heavier than yours."

I sat in my dorm room that day when these thoughts came back to my mind.

I was being so obsessive and narrow-minded.

I was seeing injury as so negative.

I was failing to see the positive.

I was failing to see that my biggest worry may be someone else's dream.

Someone else may be dreaming to have the opportunity to challenge her body, to understand her body. Someone else may be dreaming to have a chance to walk into a gym to work out. Someone else may be dreaming of the chance to know what swimming in a clean pool is like. Someone else may be dreaming of what it was like to attend a university.

How small are we in this world?
How open are we to this world?
How full of life are we in this world?
How appreciative are we of this world?
How appreciative are we that we are different?
How beautiful is it not being normal?
How important is it to **see** even on the darkest of our days?
How easy are we on ourselves?

After this realization, I started to get involved with other aspects of college. I became friends with students who were not on the team, I went out and danced, I got a work-study job. These extra aspects of my college experience were meant to ground me, and I allowed myself to explore and understand more of myself. Jen's story allowed me to see the benefit in cultivating and taking care of my identity, rather than isolating who I am to a sport.

I left my narrow-mindedness, and I began to focus on my whole identity. Try to see injury as time to rediscover yourself. A time to reinvent your identity without that thing. A time where your identity is undergoing a rebirth, a change, a transformation. Don't miss an opportunity to learn more about yourself. Again, I can be Kylene, *a* runner; not Kylene, *the* runner.

***

Take Away:

- There is no normal. Live by this, and fuel yourself with this knowledge.
- Catch yourself when you feel obsessive and narrow-minded. Recognize when your life is revolving around something, rather than that something as part of your life, and change it.
- Alter the mindset of injury...be easy on yourself.

Up Next:

- Energy was brought up a few different times in this chapter. What is energy, and how is it involved in the creation of ourselves?

CHAPTER EIGHT:

THE IMPORTANCE OF FUELING ONE'S ENERGY

Life is lived when we aren't at a deficit.

Have you ever felt your body drained at the end of the day? Your energy level past zero?

Energy is a key aspect of being a holistic athlete. Our energy levels provide us with keen insight into what our body needs, both mentally and physically.

A deficit in energy can actually be a diagnosis known as "Relative Energy Deficiency Syndrome (RED-S)." I first learned of this syndrome after interviewing Colette Richter. Colette ran at the University of Wisconsin in undergrad and then completed her masters at Oregon State University. As a 10K runner in college, she underwent a few of her own injuries that stemmed from this diagnosis. Intrigued by this topic, I examined a research article that described what RED-S entails.

The research was completed by Siobhan Statuta in "The Female Athlete Triad, Relative Energy Deficiency in Sport, and the Male Athlete Triad: The Exploration of Low- Energy Syndromes in Athletes." From this article I discovered that RED-S encompasses a wide array of individuals, including both males and females.[30] The major focus of RED-S is energy deficiency from caloric insufficiencies, and the array of health consequences that follow. The female athlete triad falls under RED-S, but the triad is more specific to females because of a lost menses.[31] Overall, athletes are not meeting caloric demands, leading to health consequences.[32]

Our body physically breaks down without calories. However, a topic this important could not just be read personally. I needed to know if the importance of energy levels was considered in the athletic world, and so, I set out to interview individuals who could explain how their low energy levels impacted their health.

I had the opportunity of interviewing Christiana Rutkowski, who is the writer behind the blog "**champions are made when no one is watching.**" Having been a runner in both undergrad and graduate school, Christiana explained how inadequate energy levels impacted her own injuries:

"I've had to deal with other sorts of 'injuries,' which have included chronically low iron levels and cycles of extreme

30 Siobhan M. Statuta, "The Female Athlete Triad, Relative Energy Deficiency in Sport, and the Male Athlete Triad: The Exploration of Low-Energy Syndromes in Athletes," *Current Sports Medicine Reports* 19, no. 2 (February 2020): 44.

31 Siobhan M. Statuta, "The Female Athlete Triad, Relative Energy Deficiency in Sport, and the Male Athlete Triad: The Exploration of Low-Energy Syndromes in Athletes," *Current Sports Medicine Reports* 19, no. 2 (February 2020): 43

32 Siobhan M. Statuta, "The Female Athlete Triad, Relative Energy Deficiency in Sport, and the Male Athlete Triad: The Exploration of Low-Energy Syndromes in Athletes," *Current Sports Medicine Reports* 19, no. 2 (February 2020): 44

fatigue and burnout. I believe the origin of those kinds of injuries manifested as a result of under-fueling and not realistically eating the amount my body needed to thrive consistently."

Christiana understood that under-fueling impacted her energy levels, ultimately leading to an injury. To undermine energy means we are undermining our own capabilities, our own vitality. I asked Christiana what she saw energy as, and she provided a beautiful, altruistic response:

"To put it simply, to me energy means the fusion of mind, body, soul in regard to something that brings you joy, passion, and where you can find gratitude and solace. As a product of these connections, you are able to be your most authentic self and reach your potential."

I appreciated hearing her response, as she is someone who values energy. Christiana just finished graduate school and now has her master's degree in clinical mental health counseling. I can assure you she is truly a positive influence, and her own personal stories can shed light on the power of energy and self-love.

A MALE'S PERSPECTIVE

Despite my interviews with female athletes, I wanted to hear a male's perspective on how energy availability and training mix together. I interviewed graduate student Nick McFarland from Monmouth University. During the interview, Nick described his own experience with low energy levels. His experience with feeling low energy levels initially stemmed from a mental component, feeling that his mind and body were not in-tuned. Nick decided to visit a sports psychologist because he thought perhaps the emotions he was feeling were in his head. Nick explained,

"Indoor came and I was not feeling great. After every workout I did not feel good. Everyone thought I was in my head, and that I needed to relax and have more fun with it. So, I saw a sports psychologist."

Outdoor came, however, and Nick continued to run below his potential. Nick furthers his story, saying:

"There was a moment that I had almost an ego death experience. I did not feel myself. I told my sports psychologist, 'I don't think there is anything wrong with me.' And he said, 'I think you found your answer, I don't think there is anything wrong with you either.' So, I had more blood tests done."

Nick knew this feeling of depleted energy was not just in his head. One of the first conditions doctors wanted to rule out for him was iron deficiency. Iron deficiency was brought up a few different times during the interviews and is a common lab value checked for runners. Despite the doctor's consideration for iron, Nick's levels came back fine. Yet, he knew something was not right and continued to advocate for himself. After many tests and doctor visits later, Nick found out he had Lyme disease.

Aside from lack of energy availability due to Lyme disease, Nick also mentioned the impact previous injuries had on his mental energy. Suffering from a stress fracture in his foot, he had to take time away from running altogether: "I was in a really deep place because I ran so fast right before the injury, and I was so close. I was super depressed after that. I was not with my team much and my roommate had also transferred, and my other teammate quit the team!"

Energy stems from both a mental and physical component, as the two coexist together. This realization for Nick has cultivated a novel perspective he now utilizes in his training. *"I'm listening to my body. That's the number one. With injuries, sometimes you don't want to believe what is going on, so you push through. When I am sore and tired, I don't go run ten to thirteen miles. I take an easy run. My biggest piece of advice—take the easy days easy, and the hard days hard. Even in high school I didn't abide by this."*

After reading the literature on energy and hearing both male and female experiences with energy, I was reminded of a memory I had back when I was a junior in high school touring different colleges. It was a Saturday morning and my *whole* family was loading up our Dodge minivan with a cooler full of water and a bag full of snacks for all six of us as we piled into the van. I am the oldest of four kids, and I was the first to embark on the college journey.

During one visit in particular, I was meeting up with one of the track coaches at a particular college. He toured me around their facility and told me about their track team, making an effort to mention the names of athletes who moved on to regionals or NCAA. At one point of the tour, he brought up injuries and how a few athletes were redshirting so they could complete a fifth year due to an injury they sustained. He said to me, "Every college runner gets hurt at some point." He stopped me for a second with the cold reality of it.

I told myself I was a maverick. I was never injured in high school, and I never had pain running. Well, he was right. Five injuries later, I had become a consistent case to his point. Today, as a physical therapist student now, I continue to credit his statement with disbelief. I strongly believe athletes can substantially control their health. After reflecting on both my own personal and educational experiences, I came down to three injury preventative measures. **Our nutrition, Our Recovery, and Our Threshold.** Considering these three measures will provide proper management of one's energy levels.

WAYS TO PROPERLY MANAGE ENERGY:

NUTRITION

I am no dietician, and so, I am not going to list the foods and portion sizes you should eat. If I learned anything as an athlete, I wish I had consumed more than I did. As a runner, I was at practice two to three hours a day running high-intensity exercises. What is not emphasized enough is that with each workout we complete, the body is breaking down. We are physically breaking down small muscle fibers, loading our bones, and dehydrating our cells.

The workout is not finished until you have refueled afterwards. The body must reabsorb nutrients at this new threshold it has reached. Each run, each game, each practice you attend, you are physically changing your body. Perhaps the change is small, but small changes over time create large distinctions. *Replenish. Replenish.* As the cautious runner I became after undergoing my first injury, I went to an orthopedic doctor to ensure I was fully healed. During my visit I asked him how to prevent future injuries. I remember him telling me, "You have to eat even when you are not hungry."

I started to incorporate his advice during my later collegiate training years. If you want to be an athlete, then you need to fuel your body like one. I learned this through trial and error, as my younger self ate three meals a day and assumed I was fine. I was naive to the drastically unhealthy blows my body was absorbing from the lack of essential nutrients it craved. I was unconsciously depriving my body of the fuel it needed to run. Food is fuel. Learn to love it.

At some point in time, "skinny is fast" was introduced into the running world. This is sad, and I hope one day athletes see the impact proper nutritional intake has on energy: both physically and mentally. I can say that I ran my fastest mile time and won a state championship when I was fueling properly and putting on a lot of muscle with my trainer, Jeff Copen. In a recent interview, Copen spoke about how the first indication that nutrition is not meeting the body's needs comes from losing one's menstrual cycle. Apart from nutrition, Copen also emphasized the importance of recovery for athletes.

RECOVERY:

Jeff Copen has been a gym owner and athletic trainer for over thirty years. He has helped over 160 athletes move on to the collegiate level to train in college and has helped 25 athletes toward becoming All Americans. He is also an independent trainer for the NHL and the NFL. Copen was an Olympic trainer for the USA Olympics from late 1990-94 in Colorado Springs, Colorado. And so, he is no stranger to the importance of training and recovery for athletes. He told me, "Distance runners are not over-trained, they are under-recovered."

What you provide to your body now will impact you later. How you recover your body during hard workouts or even hard days is important. Nutrition and recovery go hand in hand because how we fuel our bodies is representative of how long we want our bodies to run for. Personally, I want my body to run for a lifetime.

I also interviewed Coach Juli Benson due to her extensive coaching experience and her own prior experience as an Olympian in 1996. Coach Benson has coached at Air Force Academy, George Mason, Georgetown, James Madison, and University of Pennsylvania.[33] She also coached Jenny Simpson toward a gold medal in the 2011 World Championships in Daegu, South Korea, and the 2012 Olympic games.[34] Her experience invariably touches upon the importance of recovery.

Coach Benson states: "If recovery is so important that these professional athletes are risking their livelihood, their life, to do this, then that means recovery is pretty damn important. And the biggest performance enhancers you can have in college are sleep and water."

THRESHOLD

One of the most common running-related injuries is an overtraining injury. What I believe athletes fail to understand is that not only is mileage an indicator of injury, but intensity is as well. It is important to allow yourself to abridge established weekly goals when you are having a particularly difficult mental or physical week. Coach Benson mentioned how an athlete's training should work around factors that are also occurring in their life in order to limit the potential for overtraining injuries.

---

33 "Women's Track and Field: Juli Benson," Penn Athletics, accessed November 15, 2020.

34 "Women's Track and Field: Juli Benson," Penn Athletics, accessed November 15, 2020.

"Let's say for instance, Trisha can handle sixty miles a week and stay healthy and do all these workouts and everything's great, but Trisha only sleeps four hours a night. Was it the sixty miles or was it that she was running sixty miles on a body that wasn't recovered from lack of sleep?"

The great thing about sports, though, is that you are never alone. You can talk with your coach about your training and how you may need to make adjustments due to life's demands. Coach Benson furthers this idea by saying:
"I think the coach has to provide this safe space for the athlete to be able to come to you and say listen, I get it, I know I need to sleep more but I have X, Y, and Z."

Looking back, if I were to change things it would be my nutrition, my recovery, and my threshold. I can almost promise I would have come out a better runner, spending more laps on the track than in the pool cross-training. It is not easy to plan and detail every workout and run so that it matches the needs of the day, and of course we also want to train our bodies so we can race fast and make it to the big meets. But I remind you that the best pre-race training you can do is monitoring how well you are recovering and staying healthy! No race was ever won for those that could not toe the line.

I was a collegiate athlete when I learned the importance of nutrition, threshold, and recovery. However, I believe young athletes can begin to incorporate these into their own everyday lives. Allowing the body to grow strong provides increased potential for future success. Personally, high school was my most successful time running. However, despite the lack of injuries I had then, I was told my injuries occurred in college because of the choices I made in high school. I unconsciously fell toward the common false assumptions that occur in high school: more focus on mileage and training than on adequate amounts of food to refuel. And so, I set out to gather what the current high school misconceptions are.

***

Take Away:

- Monitoring energy levels is an important part of being a holistic athlete.
- We need to properly refurbish our own energy.
- Relative energy deficiency syndrome is a lack of energy due to the lack of adequate nutrition in the body.
- Nutrition. Recovery. Threshold.

Coming Up:

- Energy is important, and we need to be attuned to its value.
- **We need to consider:** How is this topic ingrained in the younger population of athletes? How can we implement this knowledge and understanding earlier on as a pillar of preventative medicine?

CHAPTER NINE:

YOUNG MISCONCEPTIONS

Have you ever wished you could travel back in time and change a decision you once made? Have you wished that you had the knowledge you have now but back then? Are you longing for an opportunity to reverse your past and focus your energy differently?

As a current physical therapy student, I feel this profession has the potential to do just this, but from a preventative medicine perspective. My goal as a future clinician is to educate young athletes on physical health, mental health, and wellness. While I hope this book can be a platform for young athletes, I know there is an even greater population of athletes who may never open this book. This remarkable profession can assist in the prevention of common, preventable injuries that stem from a lack of awareness and education on health and wellness topics.

It has been seven years since I was last in high school. (That surprised me when I wrote that.) Despite the common misconceptions about running and training I had in high school, I wanted to ensure I had a strong understanding of the thoughts and assumptions of today's runners if I hope to educate them. From my own personal high school experience, I believed in order to be the best runner I had to run...a lot. I felt cross-training or missing a run would impact my speed. I wanted to see if these misconceptions were around today, or if they had changed.

To any high school athlete reading this book, I want you to take this True or False quiz:

True or False:

1. More mileage makes you faster.
2. Taking a few days off can impact your speed.
3. Eating ice cream can impact performance.
4. Cross-training as a workout is not as good as running.
5. Practice is an opportunity to compare your pace to your teammates.

Seeking out a high school interviewee, I realized my sister, Chelsey Cochrane, was a perfect candidate. As my sister, I hoped she could be completely transparent with me. In addition, she herself has undergone a few different injuries during high school running, including stress fractures, a partial hamstring tear, and many ankle sprains. I asked Chelsey what the common themes were in high school running. What were the beliefs she felt and heard from friendly talks with other runners and on social media pages?

The statements I listed above were similar misconceptions she feels and hears. From her experience on the team and from conversing with teammates, there is a strong gravitation and belief that cross-training is not as good of a workout as running. Reflecting back on the quiz, the answer to all of those statements is <u>false.</u>

These themes were no different from the ones I felt during high school.
It has been seven years since I was last in high school.
These mental misconceptions continue to exist.
This needs to change.

Continuing with the interview, I asked Chelsey how she emotionally felt during her injuries. *"Each time I was injured, I was embarrassed. I was the one on the team who always got injured. Mentally, I felt isolated from the team, too. People would congratulate each other after each workout, and I was just there sitting on my bike watching."*

Chelsey is young to experience what many athletes at higher competitive levels feel. I had never experienced isolation from the team, or remorse from feeling left out of a workout, until I was in college. Chelsey was experiencing these emotions at a young age, as a freshman in high school. "Going to doctors was depressing. It was hard having to get an MRI when all I wanted to do was run."

This mental psyche of an injury can be carried with someone for a while. But injuries that occur at a young age can have even greater repercussions, including a heightened fear of getting injured again. In my opinion, injury at a young age can also impact one's confidence and social support during a time in their life when they are trying to fit in with society and find their own identity.

Despite the age difference between runners, the emotions that occur during injury can be similar. No matter what age, the mind is impacted. This is why I feel the physical therapy profession has an opportunity to educate young athletes. Aside from the physical injury itself, we can help prevent the mental isolation and impacted identity felt during injury by preventing the injury in the first place. How? Through adequate education. Young athletes should be growing and expanding their mind. Preventing the injury can help assist in improving one's mental health, rather than impacting it at a young age.

I feel preventative medicine strategies can be incorporated into the younger generations. In fact, "the American Physical Therapy Association (APTA) supports advocacy for prevention, wellness, fitness, health promotion, and management of disease and disability."[35] One way in which preventative medicine can ensue is through the promotion of educational programs for high school athletes. Having a physical therapist educate athletes, and even first-time coaches, can assist in the prevention of over-training, under-fueling, and poor recovery. I am a firm believer that our actions today will impact us later on. It is time we advocate for informative education at the athletic level to assist in the prevention of injuries and the mental health toll that follows.

The athletic world needs to help one another. If your teammate is injured, check in with an uplifting "Can't wait till you're back!" We can all benefit from not feeling alone, and we can all check in with one another. You can be running

---

35 "Association's Role in Advocacy for Prevention, Wellness, Fitness, Health Promotion, and Management of Disease and Disability: Policies and Bylaws," American Physical Therapy Association, last updated September 20, 2019.

on a high school team, but you are part of something even greater—the running community.

To continue on with Chelsey's story, it was not until several different injuries and many doctor visits that she finally felt she had a strong balance. Perhaps these injuries stemmed from a certain origin, such as training error, fueling, or recovery. Proper education can assist in limiting the frequency of these types of injury origins from occurring again. Today, Chelsey is a new athlete, but it took time, embarrassment, and change,

"I became more aware of how much and how fast I was running. I started cross-training more, and I saw the value in cross-training. I still have teammates who have pain in their shins but won't cross-train. They think they won't get a good workout in or will get slower...I cross-train two times a week."

Workouts are about quality and effort, not quantity. Cross-training is one of the strongest, most pivotal aspects of training if you want to take your body to the next level. By cross-training, you can work different muscles and challenge your body differently, as well as your mind. Chelsey also added, *"I also became very mindful of making sure I ate enough food. I was lacking a period for a few years, and after learning about what happened to my sister and the athlete triad, I wanted to address this early. Something was obviously not right."*

Not every high school athlete may have knowledge of the female athlete triad, but I do hope this book allows athletes to be knowledgeable of this common diagnosis that can occur in female runners. It is important to nurture your body and love your body, as it allows you to run and do what you love.

Prior to ending my interview with Chelsey, I asked her if she could make a list of everything she learned during her high school injuries and her high school running experience. She wrote the following:

1. If you cannot run for one to two days, it does not make a big difference.
2. Strength training is important.
3. Confidence wins races.
4. Cross-training is a good alternative.
5. If running feels like a job, then you should take a few days off and do something for yourself.
6. If you have pain, don't wait to stop running.

I appreciate Chelsey's advice, and not just because I am her sister. Growing up I was always away at school when she had these injuries. Interviewing her once again over Zoom made me realize the larger theme behind running: We have this opportunity to dramatically educate and help one another. Everyone's story is valid and true. We need to accept one another and strive to help one another. Running is a race to finish, but if you prepare to start you will have lifelong friends and knowledge along the way.

***

Take Away:

- To high school runners—running is a time to grow. You are challenging yourself each day and are striving to reach those fast times. I hope along the way you see how remarkable the running world is—we are here for you.
- The physical therapy profession has an opportunity to educate young athletes from a preventative medicine standpoint. Preventing injuries can assist in staving off the mental impact of injury at a young age.

Coming Up:

- I interviewed a few more runners. These interviews shed light on how prevalent a lot of these running misconceptions are, how valuable it is understanding that less is sometimes more, and why removing oneself from the training world for a day is part of the healing process.
- The next chapter I tell my last and biggest training mistake I made.

CHAPTER TEN:

LISTEN WITH GRACE

Holistic athletes Listen with Grace.

"Your mind wants to run faster, but your body hasn't caught up yet."

A coach told me this quote once, after I explained to him the sixth sense I felt when running. I had just finished describing to him my mind's capability of zoning out on my runs, allowing me to become just turbulent air. I felt proud and accomplished dropping 6:15 miles on my "easy" days. I thought, "If my mind believes it, then my body can withstand it." Many injuries later, I personally crafted my own understanding: **sometimes less *has* to be more.**

My mind always wanted to do more, but my muscles and bones were not ready yet. They needed time to adapt to the stress that came with running. Training is about quality over quantity and taking a day off rather than forcing an exercise on a depleted body is a smart training day to me. Reflecting back on my previous injury mistakes, I have my last realization: I **did too much.**

This chapter focuses on why I felt the need to complete so much volume in my training, and why I wish I had considered

gracious healing: listening to my body both mentally and physically. After interviewing a few runners, I unlock how to train appropriately during one's injury without doing too much. More specifically, I write about how to mold one's training around their environment and not the environment around one's training.

***

During my running career, I planned my cross-training exercises so I had a hard workout each and every day. I was unconsciously depleting my body of energy, believing I had to do more volume of cross-training to equate to running miles. People told me, "Ten minutes of cross-training is equivalent to one mile." What I failed to ask was, how much intensity and how many breaks?

I was motivated, and I was passionate, but I equated training to *quantity* and not *quality*. My mindset was wrong, and my body broke again...and again...and again. I was doing too much for someone who was not only an athlete. I was also a student who had classes to pass and projects to complete. Everything we do in a day is going to impact our body with varying degrees of severity. As students, we do not have the opportunity to nap several times in one day for recovery. Professionals can train at high impact, and train multiple times a day, because they operate in an environment that provides time to rest and recover.

WHY DID I FEEL THE NEED TO DO SO MUCH?

Unknowingly, at the time, I was aiming toward perfection. I was reminded of the importance of recovery and nutrition from coaches and staff, but I was too single-minded and obsessed with running that I did not consider it. I felt bad if I didn't hit the right split in a workout or if I was unable to swim for a certain duration of time. This was my mindset as a college student tackling an Ivy League education and a D1 athletic opportunity. I would see social media as a mirror into the "correct" way to do something. I felt I could do it all because other individuals were doing it all: training, getting straight As, having a significant other, and even nailing an internship.

And I am here to say this mindset is wrong.

Physical and mental sacrifices should not have to be made during training. You can be dedicated and strongly motivated while also listening to your body. If you are dedicated to your sport, you should also be dedicated to your body. Games end. Races end. Your body is forever.

WHAT IS THE OPTIMAL AMOUNT TO CROSS-TRAIN DURING OUR INJURIES?

After interviewing more than a handful of runners who have experienced injury, I found a recurring theme: "I did not know how much I was supposed to be cross-training." Athletes can use cross-training as a substitute for running. Depending on what the doctor deems safe for one's injury at the time, individuals can bike, elliptical, swim, or jog in the water as means of training without the heavy pounding from running. Cross-training provides opportunity to remain aerobically fit despite not being able to run.

One athlete who spoke about her experience with cross-training was Ryen Frazier. Ryen Frazier was a top recruit in high school as a 4x New Balance National Champion and chose to pursue her collegiate running career at North Carolina State University. When she got to NC State, her talent continued to shine. Ryen was a 2x NCAA East Regional Qualifier in the 5,000m in 2017 and in 2018.[36] She also was a 3x All ACC performer during her 2015, 2016, and 2017 cross-country season.[37]

Despite her strong athletic resume, Ryen suffered from her own running injuries, including stress fractures in both her left and right tibia and foot. These injuries led her toward cross-training when she was unable to run. Reflecting on her freshman year training methods during injury, she stated: *"I definitely cross-trained harder than I should have, not knowing what the right amount was. College also had so many resources, so I thought, why not use them? If this is the practice time anyway, I may as well."*

Aside from not knowing how much to cross-train, athletes also felt a disconnect with their cross-training workouts. Many athletes noted how their coaches did not prescribe an exact protocol to follow when cross-training. This left the athlete feeling confused and uncertain if they were doing enough. It is extremely rare that a dedicated and motivated athlete will respond to uncertainty by doing less.

In addition, I noted how many athletes struggled emotionally when cross-training by themselves. Several interviewees brought up their times during aqua jogging—a running exercise performed in the water where individuals pump their arms quickly while also moving their legs as if they were running. A few athletes stated they would jump into the pool to train and then have to get out because they felt sad. They were disconnected from running, the team, and all familiar aspects of their driving passion.

---

36 "2020 Cross Country Roster: Ryen Frazier," North Carolina State University Athletics, Accessed January 31, 2021.

37 Ibid.

I personally remember aqua jogging and staring at the big clock inside the pool at UPenn. I told my sister, "I was convinced time went backwards when I aqua jogged." Some winter mornings I would leave my apartment wishing I could have a taste at a normal college athlete's life: one where I wasn't consistently staring at the big clock in the pool.

GRACIOUS HEALING:

I wish I knew I didn't have to force myself on days when I was mentally and physically fatigued. When you feel your feet moving slowly toward the pool, and you question if your goggles are fogging up from the pool air or your own tears, I challenge you to say "thank you" out loud.

Thank you. Your body and your mental health are signaling that you need a day away. Our bodies are constantly providing us with information, but unconsciously we may ignore it. Most of the time, it is okay to ignore laziness, and on some days, working out for thirty minutes can be beneficial. On those mentally isolating, demoralizing days, though, I challenge you to say thank you. Thank your body for making you aware of the fact you have to focus on *you*. Instead of going to the pool that day, sit in the sun, read a book for thirty minutes, do something for yourself, and know the pool will still be there tomorrow.

My friends, healing is not supposed to be sad. Our bodies are sensitive, unconsciously responding to everything in our environment. Be sensitive to it.

Healing is beautiful.

Tell yourself this as you walk away from the gym that day. Your once-injured body is now healing. Allow its recovery.

Appreciate its resilience. Perhaps embark on this time in your life where you had to slow down as an awakening. Allow your body to become strong, valuable, and important.

A quote was said best by Yale runner Dana Klein: "Does the injury process have to be that sad? There must be another way."

No it does not.

And yes, there is.

HOW CAN WE BEGIN TO IMPROVE THE HEALING PROCESS? HOW CAN WE IMPROVE OUR APPROACH TO CROSS-TRAINING AND FEEL CONFIDENT WITH OUR TRAINING?

Ryen Frazier spoke about her decision to step back and reflect on her own personal cross-training habits: *"I would definitely say I cross-trained the most my freshmen year...looking back, I'm like, mentally that wasn't a break for you. I think my body was like, 'Hey, let me chill for a little bit.'"*

After trial and error, Ryen began to change her outlook on how much cross-training was necessary. Her second injury occurred her senior year of cross-country.

"I approached cross-training so differently than I had four years before and I was probably the most fit I had ever been off of cross-training. I started at a low level and I created a calendar that I shared with my coach. I sat down with her and told her, this is what I am thinking, and I would make a workout for myself in the pool. This document was shared with other people who got hurt...I now at least had a plan!"

Ryen's story indicates the importance of structure and organization during both cross-training and the healing process. Sitting down with her coach and creating a calendar of workouts provided her with both goals and confidence in her training. Ryen also decreased the amount of cross-training she was doing and focused on quality: "Otherwise I would go to the pool and be like, what am I going to do today, or am I going to get in today?"

Ryen also mentioned how the workouts your teammates do may not be the best for *you*: "Very different types of training work for different people. Finding what works for you and a coach, that also responds well to your body, is what works."

Stress Manifestation and Injuries

Apart from the external aspects of training—the minutes and types of cross-training we decide to do—there is also an internal aspect that impacts training: stress. Stress can be difficult to control at times, but it is proven to impact how the athlete will heal and respond to their environment. It was noted in a few of the interviews I conducted how much of an impact stress had on the athlete's training and injury. A large portion of this stress stemmed from rigorous schedules and other environmental factors affecting the athlete's life apart from running.

From a schedule standpoint, I gained insight from one athlete who learned how to adapt her training to her environment. Her name is Alison Nicolosi. Alison Nicolosi is on the track and field and cross-country team at Moravian College, class of 2021. As a nursing major, she has 5:00 a.m. clinicals and does not get back to campus until 4:00 p.m., which means endless hours on her feet all day. I asked Alison how she adapted her training around her heavy academic and clinical schedule.

Alison explained: "Tuesdays I was up so early, and I knew that day at practice had to be an easy mileage day for me. I did whatever my legs could do that day. And that season ended up being my most successful."

Completing a heavy training workout on the same day she was on her feet treating patients would have led her to either injury or slower times on the track. This balance did not occur overnight, as she had to work with her coach to establish a training routine.

"I ended up having to write my schedule down for my coach so he could see the lack of time I had. I also had to talk to my coach about not being able to do doubles on these days. It was physically too much for a college student trying to balance a clinical schedule."

Our bodies are precious, and this was something I failed to acknowledge and appreciate during my early years in college. Unlike Alison, I did not adapt my schedule to my training.

I was naive.
I was young.
I am me.

From an environmental stressor perspective, Ryen explains how her training was impacted by the stress she was feeling: "I think my injuries were stress related as well and explains why it took so long to heal."

Ryen Frazier was not the only athlete to mention a possible relationship between stress and injury. Colette Richter, a runner from Wisconsin University, furthered this idea with her own personal experience with stress and injury. As I mentioned previously, Colette ran in undergrad at the University of Wisconsin, and then later went to Oregon State University, where she ended up fulfilling her master's in plant breeding and genetics. She too believes one of her injuries was purely stress related:

"I had a really tight calf. No matter how much physical therapy I did or massage, it did not help. I believe that something emotional in your life will manifest into a certain part of your body. And I was dealing with a lot of stuff at that time and felt really stressed."

"At the time, I had been seeing a psychologist to help with my anxiety. I had a busy day with classes and cross-training. I was rushing to my psychologist appointment on my bike in the rain when all of the sudden my bike tire got caught in a crack and I fell. I wasn't hurt, but I felt lucky I didn't hit my head or fall into the road. It was a wake-up call. I couldn't keep running around like a chicken with its head cut off anymore. I opened the door to the session room with blood on my legs and said, 'I need a change.' I had to directly deal with my anxiety, and the things that were causing my anxiety, to fall out of this heightened, desirous control I felt I needed to have. It was after dealing with my problems more directly and working hard on my anxiety that my mental and physical health began to improve."

I looked further into the relationship between stress and injuries. An article done by Philipp Laux and colleagues, titled "Recovery-Stress Balance and Injury Risk in Professional Football Players: A Prospective Study," looked into the impact stress and recovery had on athletic injury.[38] Twenty-two professional German football players were used, and approximately sixteen months of injury records were assessed. During this time, participants completed the Recovery-Stress Questionnaire for Athletes (RESTQ-Sport).[39]

This questionnaire has different scales that can predict injury risk.[40] From the study, the most common injuries were muscular and tendinous, followed by joint and ligament.[41] From the scales of the RESTQ questionnaire, fatigue, sleep quality, distributed breaks, and injury all had significant associations for injury within the subsequent months.[42] While this study has more specified details, I personally realized the importance of screening athletes on their personal perceptions of their recovery and stress parameters.

I personally feel if an athlete is undergoing many injuries, it can be beneficial having that athlete talk with a physician, coach, or psychologists. This is especially true for freshman, who can be greatly impacted by the novel environment, training, and academic stress. I conversed with my coach during my freshman year about a stressor in my life that was not running related. He helped me tremendously, and I

---

38 Philipp Laux, Bertram Krumm, Martin Diers, and Herta Flor, "Recovery–Stress Balance and Injury Risk in Professional Football Players: A Prospective Study," *Journal of Sports Sciences* 33, no. 20 (2015): 2141.

39 Philipp Laux, Bertram Krumm, Martin Diers, and Herta Flor, "Recovery–Stress Balance and Injury Risk in Professional Football Players: A Prospective Study," *Journal of Sports Sciences* 33, no. 20 (2015): 2141-2142.

40 Philipp Laux, Bertram Krumm, Martin Diers, and Herta Flor, "Recovery–Stress Balance and Injury Risk in Professional Football Players: A Prospective Study," *Journal of Sports Sciences* 33, no. 20 (2015): 2144.

41 Ibid.

42 Philipp Laux, Bertram Krumm, Martin Diers, and Herta Flor, "Recovery–Stress Balance and Injury Risk in Professional Football Players: A Prospective Study," *Journal of Sports Sciences* 33, no. 20 (2015): 2145.

realized how much better my body felt physiologically after I validated the stress. Similar to Ryen and Colette, stress can manifest itself in the body, and I personally feel finding a way to expel that stress allows the body to feel better.

In summary, having reflected on my previous cross-training methods, I see how hard I pushed myself during a time that I needed to heal. There is power in listening to your body with grace and intuition. Holistic athletes truly listen with grace.

Through this healing, may we also continue to train our minds to see the badass athletes we truly are! We are intensely and vigorously training our endurance, strengthening our muscles, and ice-bathing our tired legs...but are we training our greatest organ with the same degree of repetition and passion? Our brain.

***

Take Away

- Listen with Grace
- Less sometimes **has** to be more in order for our body to heal and adjust appropriately.
- Create a cross-training calendar and share it with your coach. Now you have goals and a purpose!
- Cultivate a training schedule that works for your environment.
- Validate your stress.
- Say "thank you" to your body more often.

Coming Up:

- How do we train a mind at the level we train our physical body?

CHAPTER ELEVEN:

MENTAL IMAGINATION

The mind of holistic athletes is strong, important, and loved.

I must enlighten you with the most powerful source we have to win...our mind. You will lose 100 percent of the races if you fail to train your mind. Toeing the line and not believing you will win means you won't. Our perception of ourselves and our own strengths is a huge component of being successful.

In my previous chapter, I mentioned the importance of timely, gracious healing for our body. I spoke of the mental impact injury incurs and the relative role stress can play in the healing process. I have yet to mention how powerful perception and intuitive thoughts are on the success of our training and races. How can we begin to tackle the mental psyche of injuries? By training the mind. Your mind must be trained as much as your physical body.

***

Prior to every race, I told myself, "I am going to win." Stepping onto that line, I already won. I was an underdog during most of my college races, with the slowest time in my heat.

Yet, my mind didn't know that, and I never let it. I envisioned myself winning before the race even began. On the bus ride to the meet, I was winning. During the warm-up, I was winning. By the time the gun went off signaling the start of the race, I had already won...thirty different times. When I stepped foot on that line, my mind was already sending neural responses toward my muscles; now all I had to do was run.

I started to train my mind in high school. On the bus ride to meets, I could stare endlessly outside the window. The trees and cars passing by on the highway were superficial abstracts to my eye. I was so completely immersed in my own vision that all other stimuli melted into oblivion. I was imagining myself racing, uniform on and the crowd yelling. I was mentally running the race before it even began, and my body was able to physiologically respond with an increased heart rate and clammy hands. When it was time to really race, my mind and body had already lived through the pre-race nerves. I could now be exclusively focused on just the race, without the distraction from my pre-race nerves.

Sixteen seconds to glory. My dad and I wrote this down on a piece of paper before I had my first state meet. Sixteen seconds was the time I took to run the last 100-meter straightaway during the mile race. Only sixteen seconds till it was all over. This was the phrase I repeated to myself before and during every race I ran.

Those seconds became my physical strength during the part of the race where it turned all mental, when my legs screamed with pain and my lungs gasped for oxygen. I become a state champion not out of talent or luck, but out of pure mental strength. During the 2014 New Jersey State Championship meet, I won the 1,600m race even before my bus arrived at the Toms River Bubble in Southern New Jersey.

I was using a form of "motor imagery." This term was never in my repertoire until I heard it in physical therapy school. In a study done by Corina Schuster and colleagues, titled "Best Practice for Motor Imagery: A Systematic Literature Review on Motor Imagery Training Elements in Five Different Disciplines," motor imagery is considered the mental imagination of body parts moving.[43] Mental practice is another phrase used, and it can be considered an umbrella term for the different types of mental trainings used.[44] These mental trainings can be used in specialties apart from sports, including music, medicine, and education.[45]

JULI BENSON: FORMER OLYMPIAN, NOW RUNNING COACH.

Mental training strategies were not utilized by me alone. Mental training is what Olympian and track coach Juli Benson used throughout her training, particularly when she was injured. Training for the Olympics requires strength, grit, and enormous stress on the body. Coach Benson was no stranger to injury, and she too has been sidelined because of injuries that kept her distant from her training and teammates. Her training was fierce, consistent, and on point, yet she explains how her mental game was weak, frail, and riddled with fear.

---

43 Corina Schuster et al., "Best Practice for Motor Imagery: A Systematic Literature Review on Motor Imagery Training Elements in Five Different Disciplines," *BMC Medicine* 9, no. 75 (June 2011): 2

44 Ibid.

45 Ibid.

In college, Benson had to complete an independent study requirement with a sports psychologist in order to receive her master's. She initially felt the visits were tedious and time consuming and was not truly investing herself into the sessions. While working on her master's, Benson was also competitively running. However, she failed to understand the training she also needed for her mind.

"My friend said, 'I thought you were working with a sports psychologist,' and I was like, 'Oh yeah, I am;' she's like, 'Well, you still sound really, really negative about your running.' When she said that, a light bulb went off, and I realized I should really invest in this [sports psychologist training], and so I did."

How we speak, love, and care for ourselves influences our mind and execution of our everyday tasks. The earlier you realize this, the sooner you will see the results. Excited and empowered, she decided to take advice from her sports psychologists and really invest her mind into the sessions.

The snow that January, however, carried with it something heavier than dense, packed water. Coating the track that winter for Coach Benson was something more widespread than the six lanes: Benson was diagnosed with a femoral stress fracture.

"I got injured the January before the Olympic trials. I went into my sports psychologist's office and I said, 'Thanks so much for trying to help me, but you know it's over, because I'm going to be out for six or eight weeks, and how am I ever going to get back to make the team, there's no way, so thanks.'...He told me, 'It's January, you're going to be fine.'"

Injury is a pivotal time to engage mental training in conjunction with physical. One of the first mental training tasks the sports psychologist developed with Coach Benson was feeling a part of the team despite not being able to run with it. He wanted her to train with the team without running. This task particularly targets the mental isolation athletes feel when distant from teammates during injury. Taking his advice, Coach Benson found herself grabbing the stationary bike from the gym and bringing it out onto the track anytime there was a workout.

"I would have to pedal as hard as I possibly could every time my teammates did an interval. If they were doing mile repeats, I had to go all out on the bike. It was crazy, but I could watch them, and having myself biking while also watching my teammates made me feel as if I just got done with that workout when I got off the bike."

Coach Benson was undergoing a form of mental training—envisioning, watching, and completing a strenuous task despite doing something different. Benson mentally envisioned herself completing that workout, even though she physically was working her body differently. Heart rate is just a reading, but confidence needs to be felt. This type of training provided her confidence, as her mind connected to her teammates and their workout.

The second task the sports psychologist had her complete was disassociating running from this prized, gold-standard aspiration.

"Let's say I was supposed to do a tempo run; he wanted me three or four times that day to say, 'Hahaha, I don't have to go out in this cold weather, I don't have to run today.' I would trick myself into thinking not running can be a good thing."

Coach Benson developed another strategy of her own that helped train her mind. This one was more of a visual but also something she physically could hold and read.

"If my workout was ten 400s and I hit the time on eight of them, I wrote eight things down. If one or two things didn't go the way I wanted, I ripped it up and threw it away. By the end of the season, I had this bag full of things that went well."

The benefit of this task is being able to physically hold a bag of positive accomplished events that can be viewed every day. Carrying this bag with you on race day is a visual reminder for how resilient and strong you are. Look at all those accomplishments and tell yourself, "I deserve to win."

Of all the different mental trainings Benson stated, this last one is my favorite:

> "Anytime a negative thought came in, he had me say stop out loud."

Let the faces turn toward you in public, and let the birds silence their chirp. Allow your own voice to inhibit the negative, because you're the one in control of your thoughts. That spring, Coach Benson qualified for the 1996 Olympic games in the 1,500m.

CAMARADERIE DURING INJURY:

Aside from just mental training, injured athletes also need socialization. Humans are very social creatures, yet this socialization component is impacted during injury. Coach Benson touched upon the importance of surrounding oneself when it comes to injury with four to five individuals one can truly trust.

"You should really try to drown out the outside noise. Everyone's going to try to give you their opinion. You have got to find

a team of people that you trust, and that could be your team doctor, nutritionists, your coach, and your parents, whoever it is. You're going to get so many people that just volunteer and give advice, and that can make you go crazy."

There is no need to go through this injury alone. As someone who used to keep a lot of emotions bottled in, I find so much clarity after I vent to someone. I feel confident and less insecure of my emotions after someone has listened to them. A key aspect to socialization is involving oneself in something non-running related. Coach Benson mentions the value of using standard practice time to "get better."

"Do something to mentally get you away from the fact that you're not able to do what you love to do. I think that can really help you with your peace of mind."

Overall, train your mind. Be confident and speak kindly to yourself, as this injury is temporary. All injuries are the body's way of telling us it needs to heal. Allow it and embrace it.

After reflecting back on my own "sixteen seconds to glory" experience, I realized the power that can be gained from imagination. As children we use so much imagination. We buy "fake food," which is really plastic, painted to resemble any variety of food groups. These plastic foods to a child represent the ingredients of a meal prepared in a well-equipped, make-believe kitchen. I even used to collect leaves to play with and picture them as flowers. I fear as we've grown older we have forgotten the success imagination grants us.

I like to think of motor imagery as a way of using our inherent imaginative power to reach our goals. Imagine yourself winning a race. Take it a step further and put on your uniform top, your spikes, and feel your heart rate and nerves as if you were stepping foot on the line. Envision the crowd surrounding the track or the game. What is the weather like? Which state are you in? Is there a certain smell to the air? Develop this scene and live it. Tell yourself you will win, and if you do it right, your mind will not know what reality is and what is imaginative.

***

Take Away:

- Take time to practice motor imagery. Live the event before it even occurs.
- Stop negative thoughts before they are processed.
- When you cannot train due to injury, trick your mind into believing not running is a good thing.
- Write down the good and rip up the bad.

Coming Up:

- Apart from mentally remaining in the game, how can we also do this physically?

CHAPTER TWELVE:

SELFISHLY, SELFLESS

I lost count of the number of laps that I watched from the bleachers in Franklin Field while sidelined. However, I can account for the number of races where I felt a steadfast love for running: five. In my seven years of running, there were only five races when I truly felt this faithful love for track and field. I reflected on what it was about these five races that made them so vividly rememberable; these were the ones I replayed in my head when I was injured...and I was injured a lot.

This realization allowed me to understand why maintaining involvement in one's sport during injury is important. In my previous chapters I outlined the importance of mental and physical healing, yet I have not covered how individuals can maintain involvement when injured. During the interviews there was one athlete in particular who provided keen insight and appreciation for being with a team, despite not being able to play after an injury: Lauren Beecher.

Lauren Beecher knew how to read the game. As a two-time sports player at Dickinson College, she adapted her motor skills to take on both lacrosse and volleyball. Going into her senior year of college, she decided to narrow in on her favorite sport, volleyball. As team captain, she knew what was required of her in order to be a leader to her team. Years prior, Lauren had battled both a bad ankle sprain and a bad virus another year, keeping her off the court...but not this year.

The countless hours during her injury away from the court allowed her to better appreciate the game. Watching the round ball glide in the air, awaiting the swift movements from players to prevent its fall, was her passion. And so, it comes as no surprise how excited she was for the first game of her senior season to be a tournament in Puerto Rico.

Lauren recalls: "I remember my aunt and my cousin were coming to watch me play for the first time. It had been four years; I was so excited. My whole family flew down to the game."

The sounds of the stadium silenced, watching as the ball rose in the air, signaling the start of the match. The dynamic movement and sounds of the volleyball echoed inside the arena, as players jumped to rebound the ball with their own swift movements. Of these players was Lauren:

"And then I tore my ACL. My season was over after one-eighth of the way in."

However, Lauren was hopeful. In those prized moments between injury and diagnosis, Lauren hoped the pain was not indicative of what was occurring inside her knee:

"There was two weeks before I got the MRI, and my roommate and I were both trying to stay hopeful. She was my best friend and also on the team." Lauren was hoping that perhaps the pain she was feeling was just a bad bruise, or even just some slight inflammation that would decrease. "But then I got the results, and I tore my ACL, my meniscus, and cracked the cartilage."

Hearing a diagnosis of ACL tear is devastating. When an individual hears they tore their ACL, they are also hearing they will need a year of rehab and strength training if they undergo surgery. Lauren, however, was also hearing that her collegiate volleyball career was over. Despite the fact that she had already suffered from injuries in the past, she still was injured again. The difficult part of sports is how much chance is involved. There is no referee that tells you, "Okay, you were injured this year, you will be fine next year." Stepping into a game, race, or match is really stepping into a game of chance.

Lauren's personal recovery from injury sheds light on how she moved forward with her diagnosis:

"Right as I got the news I had my crying spell. But after a while you can't dwell on that for too long and you have to just accept your new role. There is nothing I could have done to change it. After I got the surgery, I was a month out from getting the news and I came to terms with it, and my teammates had come to terms with it as well. There was just no reality of me returning, and I had to switch my mindset."

Lauren's team missed her physical presence on the court, along with her positive demeanor. Yet, Lauren decided to take on a different role that allowed her to be both a part of the team and to feel a part of the game she loved: "My position was filled by a freshman who was not really prepared yet. I remember trying to utilize my time off and take her under my wing as best as I could and just give her some pointers."

Lauren attended practices to work one-on-one with her new teammate. She also assisted the coaches with structuring and assisting the practices. Lauren found healing through the selfless act of helping her teammate. She reoriented her focus away from her own injury, and instead toward how she could benefit the team. It takes grit to reorient one's focus away from one's injury; it takes grit to be selfless. The knowledge we cultivate from injuries is ours—that is, until we share it.

It was not just Lauren who was selfless, though. Her team and coaches are the epitome of how an athlete should be treated during trying times. The team coach provided Lauren with tasks to do around the court and during the games, including taking notes on the sidelines for him. Did he really need them? Lauren could never tell, but she still appreciated it. The way she puts it: "He made it seem as if it was important for me to do this during the game so I could stay engaged and give advice to people. Whenever I was on the sidelines and someone would come off, I would talk to her if she was having a down moment."

As the season continued, Lauren began to hear her name announced as assistant coach. This was a moment in time when she felt full of gratitude. The day of Lauren's ACL surgery was also the day her team had a game, but her team never forgot her: "My whole team was incredible. I got the surgery on the day of a game and then my mom flew in and got a hotel because my apartment wasn't that accessible for crutches. While I was waiting at the hospital, my coach, team, and assistant coach all surprised me!"

There is power in being selfless during selfish times. Life itself is selfish, throwing us into events that we cannot control but are expected to deal with. The phrase "full of life" is generally thought to include being energetic, outgoing, adventurous, and spontaneous. Personally, I think to feel "full of life" is a selfless act. To be full of something that has so much unpredictability and chance is selfless. Life encompasses the experiences of others, strangers, friends, family, etc. If everyone was full of life, then no individual would truly feel alone. I challenge all those presently injured to attempt a selfless act. Put your energy toward something you can control, something you will find success in.

As I am writing this, Lauren is at Drexel University studying in its physical therapy program. After undergrad, though, she decided to travel the world. Going to Switzerland and then Ireland, she rented out a van with one of her best friends and explored the countries' green landscapes, friendly citizens, and organic culture. Later, she decided to stay in London and spent two nights independently, enriching herself in the beauty of British history and culture. Adventurous and fearless, Lauren has an appreciation for the people around her and a curiosity for the places she has yet to travel.

However, despite the fearless nature others find so admirable, she still holds a piece of fear:

"One thing I've noticed is I've had multiple people try to have me join a league, but I have not been able to bring myself to do it. And I don't think it's because I'm like scared I'll be bad with the skills; it's more a huge mental barrier that I'm scared of getting hurt again, or maybe it's me bringing up all the memories that I kind of pushed away." After having a traumatic injury like Lauren did, it is common for athletes to feel fearful when returning to their game.

Lauren is fearless. She challenged herself to travel abroad, touring countries in a van, studying different cultures, and experiencing new aspects of life. She even embarked on solitary adventures to prove to herself that she is capable. Throughout her injury, Lauren has been selfless. The challenges she has had to face have been inspiring, worthy of both recognition and appreciation. To put the needs of others above herself, the injured player, is not an easy task. One day my hope for Lauren is that she will be selfish and allow herself the exhilaration of jumping, knowing she will land safely and injury-free.

MY PERSONAL RETURN TO RUNNING:

Personally, I was challenged with the return to sport myself. After my fifth injury I took a long hiatus from running. After I graduated from the University of Pennsylvania, I physically had to remove myself from running altogether. The thought of pounding my sneakers on the ground led me to believe my bones would shatter any second. I hid my running sneakers for a long time. I knew I had just undergone four years of hardship, pain, and love...It was time for my body to rest.

When the thought of running returned to my mind, I started slow...I began walking. I was doing everything I could similar to running: listening to music, wearing sneakers, and hitting start on my Garmin watch. But I was still not in free flight...I physically could not take off. My mind was not ready, and so, neither was my physical body. Running is a series of catching ourselves before we fall. At that time in my life, I couldn't trust that I could prevent another fall, another injury. I did not have the energy in me to second-guess every run, every pace, every meal I ate.

However, I soon got selfish. I missed running and I wanted it; I deserved to do what I love. My return to running happened in Long Beach Island, New Jersey. Life at the beach always relaxes me. The streets are flat, and so many other individuals are out running, walking, and biking before hitting the beach with their beach chairs. I decided I felt so at ease that I wanted to try running again. I began running one minute on, one minute off. I gradually invaded my unconscious fears and started to allow the blood to enrich my muscles and veins. I started with just ten minutes total.

When I finished, I felt it...I felt the runner's high again. More importantly, I felt myself again. I felt an aspect to my identity was gradually creeping back in. Those ten minutes were not indications for the amount of time I ran, but the amount of time I confronted an unconscious fear. This is my life. I do not want to live a fearful one, but rather an appreciative one—appreciative of the minutes I was able to run that day, not the minutes of running I have missed in my lifetime.

HEALING THE MIND THROUGH SPOKEN WORDS:

In addition, overcoming injuries is not just fearful; it can also be depressing. As an athlete who underwent five different injuries, who spent countless hours alone in a pool, and who struggled with validating my emotions, I wished I sought out someone to talk to. I used to write when I felt I needed to get emotions off my mind, but writing did not suffice. A study referenced from Gulliver and colleagues, titled "Barriers and Facilitators to Mental Health Help-Seeking for Young Elite Athletes: A Qualitative Study," found that sixteen to twenty-three-year-old elite athletes stated stigma was one of the number-one reasons as to why athletes did not seek help, as well as lack of mental health literacy and previous negative experiences.[46]

---

46 Amelia Gulliver, Kathleen M. Griffiths, and Helen Christensen, "Barriers and Facilitators to Mental Health Help-Seeking for Young Elite Athletes: A Qualitative Study," *BMC Psychiatry* 12, no. 157 (September 2012): 5-6.

I wish I had talked to someone. At the time, however, I was struggling with validation. I lacked mental health literacy because prior to college I was always happy, and I was never injured. I consistently had feelings of euphoria and fullness throughout my running career. I went to a remarkable high school, where I still hold so much value and appreciation for the teachers I had, my guidance counselor, my coaches, and my principal. My injury process in college was the first time in my life that I was truly unhappy.

I always say, *"If I could go back I would not change the fact that my injuries happened."* I counter that statement because if I could go back, I would tell my young self that how I was feeling was not normal. Those depressive days could have been altered had I talked to someone. There is so much power in taking action toward better days...Do not be afraid to use your voice.

***

Take Away:

- Be Selfish: Feel your injury and absorb your emotions.
- Then Be Selfless: Healing can occur through touching the hand of someone else. Healing hands.
- Then Be Selfish Again when you feel it is time to return back to your game.
- Use your voice and seek help when needed. You are not alone.

Upcoming:

- The most recent, real events of my life. Where I am today, and where I hope to be tomorrow.

PART THREE:

THE BEAUTY IN THE BETWEEN.

These last three chapters are closest to my real-time self. I am now in physical therapy school, and I am no longer a runner at Penn. These last chapters are the most recent emotions I had—validated, raw, and real. I leave them to you.

CHAPTER THIRTEEN:

MY PRESENT IDENTITY

Dear Past,
Goodbye, and farewell.
Sincerely,
The Present

***

I recently became enamored with removing myself from the past. I have nestled my mind into something far more rewarding...the present. Before I reached this mental framework, I struggled. Earlier on in the book, I spoke about my new mindset: one that sees more than the eyes, a mindset that thinks optimally despite life not being optimal. This mindset is what allowed me to arrive to my present identity; however, I did not arrive here overnight.

As I have mentioned before, after undergrad I began physical therapy graduate school at Drexel University, not far from UPenn's campus. In graduate school, we cover many topics ranging from pediatrics to geriatrics and from muscular injuries to neurological ones. However, there was one topic in particular that left me reminiscing on my past...my female athlete triad.

I know I talked about this topic extensively during the beginning of the book, but I need readers to understand how unsettled I was with my past...for a while. I purposely wanted to place this chapter toward the end of the book because this regret has only recently left my mind. From the outside looking in, I may come off as confident, organized, and fully fine with my past. If I am being fully transparent, I did struggle, and it took time until I removed the pain I felt from my past.

When I entered physical therapy school, I was still trying to improve my bone density. My bone density at one point indicated osteopenia, a level very close to osteoporosis. I had lectures in school describing the possible onset of osteoporosis in women after menopause, and yet, here I was a twenty-three-year-old woman with the same diagnosis on my medical chart. I felt so distant from racing, yet so present in the diagnosis.

I was scared that I would never have strong bones again, and that my young, naive, twenty-year-old-self made sacrifices I could not undo just so that I could run in circles. Feeling a sense of regret for my past was difficult to manage. I viewed the Kylene in undergrad as someone distant...a stranger.

My professor continued on with her lecture, and I knew in the back of my mind I was a sample case for this topic. I wanted to tell my professor, "It took four years until I finally got it right. Four full years of trial and error, injury after injury, until I finally found a threshold that allowed me to perform, race, and still be healthy!" Why was I so persistent to get back on the track? I asked myself this many times. Until a friend of mine finally told me,

"Kylene, you need to stop living in the past."

This was a wake-up call for me. I am only human, and I was a Division I track athlete who loved the emotion and apparent longevity that came with running. I trained to race, I wanted to win, and I loved the sport. I was a female: a strong, resilient female athlete who would do anything to run and be with my team. I will always love running.

The regretful emotions I felt after I graduated were lessened after I spoke with former UPenn track and field runner Laura Steel, who is now a medical student. Today, Laura attends Sidney Kimmel Medical School. I wanted to speak with someone who was also pursuing a career in the health field and who had experienced injuries in college.

I learned Laura went through a similar story in regard to the female athlete triad. She mentioned how one year in particular she lost weight and had to stop running until she could get the weight back on. She also suffered from various injuries, including IT band syndrome and a stress fracture in her tibia during her senior cross-country season.

Her tibial stress fracture in particular was a memory she would not forget. Despite having pain in her tibia at practice, she wanted to remain positive and motivated since the following weekend was the championship cross-country meet at Princeton University. Come race day, there was a heavy snowfall that covered the entire course. Runners were gliding through the terrain and racing through puddles of water. Laura had another challenge to this race; she had a stress fracture in her tibia and was racing on it in the middle of a snowstorm.

Laura explained, "It was a bad day and I had to drop out of the race." As the conversation continued, I began to tell

Laura about the pained regret I still had for my past, having put my body through so many injuries. She paused, and then told me,

"For a lot of us, rarely are there college runners who go on to professional runners. For most of us, college running is a time to learn about yourself, your teammates, and create experiences. And you know, our experience running will influence our future careers. Your future is not based on your mile personal record...It is about the journey and what you learn about yourself."

I asked Laura if being in the medical field has influenced her opinion and thoughts on running. She said that it was actually her experiences running that inspired her to apply to medical school after learning about women's health in college: "I actually thought it was a good thing, and that it was common for other runners to not get their period either."

The doctors Laura saw at Penn educated her and would draw out the feedback mechanisms of the brain and educated her on amenorrhea (loss of a period). Laura was inspired and wondered if other runners knew the same. Laura is currently on her way toward becoming an ob-gyn.

"Yeah, in the back of my head I was like, women's health is important. Women need to be more involved in their health and know what things mean."

After speaking with Laura, I saw how ironic it all seemed. I spent four years focused on the run, not realizing I had a future life and future opportunities ahead. Four years of overcoming injuries, and where was I in terms of running now? I was not professional, and I was not seated and upheld on some infamous record book that would last a lifetime. I was, however, on my way toward becoming a healthcare provider. Life comes full circle, and I was ready to step back in, only this time as the provider, not the patient.

If I could go back in time to the beginning, I would sit my younger self down and tell her, "You need to slow down."
I would tell her to adjust and acclimate my training so that I could do less quantity, and more quality.
I would tell her to adjust and acclimate my eating so that I was eating enough, both quantity and quality.
I would tell her to not sacrifice her health for one race that lasts five minutes
I would tell her to live and work toward a body that can allow me to race forever.

Today, I am happy for the body that stopped me then. The body that allowed me to open my eyes and understand that the norm that I thought was normal was not. I am happy for the body that led me *toward* the person I am today, and I appreciate my past because it allowed me to arrive *where* I am today. And because I was so unsettled with my past, I truly changed. I have grown a different perspective on life, one that realizes how the moments we are in now create the thoughts of our future self. I want my future self to be happy.

***

Remind yourself that college is a time to learn about yourself. Do not sit with regret as I did for months or years afterwards. Remind yourself that with every injury, every mistake, we learn and we grow. College is a time for growth, no matter what branch takes off. And if you continue to feel guilt or feel afraid, remind yourself—your body is constantly undergoing change. Allow it, embrace it, and realize change is important. If the universe is so grand and large that the day on the calendar has to change every day, we can change too.

I am grateful, I am inspired, I am *still* a runner.

CHAPTER FOURTEEN

THE LAST RUN

2017-2018 Winter Track Season
Senior Year at University of Pennsylvania

***

I never envisioned my last race.
But when it occurred, it was my intuition that told me.

I wanted to place this chapter toward the end. This race is the last memory I have in a Penn uniform, and it was the hardest for me to write. This is the chapter of my life when I learned **my race was finished.**

I hardly ran my last summer of college. I had just spent the previous spring rehabbing my double plantar fasciitis injury, and I feared starting again. I was anxious about both the idea of pain and of physically breaking my body again.

The start to my senior year cross-country season that fall was easy. My coach wanted me to come back gradually, and I appreciated him for that. The whole summer prior to cross-country, I did not run any speed workouts. I simply did light mileage once I was given the green light that I was cleared to run again. My first actual speed workout was our first cross-country race that season.

During this time, I was also completing applications for graduate school, applying to over a dozen schools in hopes just one would pick me to attend physical therapy school. **At this point in my life, running was not my priority.** I went to college so I could eventually have a career I was passionate about, and so that I could attend graduate school to reach that career. My future and my applications were my priority.

I pushed running aside, despite showing up for practices. I never did any doubles, and I never ran over five miles. I was grazing the line of unhealthy and had stepped over it too many times. I told myself, *"Just make it to the bubble."* The "bubble" was erected over the soccer fields at Penn every winter so that athletes had a warm location to run and train. Penn did not have an indoor track at the time, and this bubble was a visual indication that you were training for a winter sport. I hardly was ever able to run in that bubble during my time at Penn due to my injuries.

The visual was there, and I saw the bubble anytime I walked over the bridge on Walnut Street. But too many times I had to look away, knowing once again I was not able to set foot inside. I was so happy when I completed my senior year cross-country season in one piece and had finally made it to the winter track season...I made it to the bubble.

That winter, I continued to run very low mileage. I did not want to over-train and risk injury once again. I wanted to remain physically healthy so I could step foot on the track and show off my potential. I wished I could do what my teammates did, but I knew I had to accept myself for how I was built. I was cautious, and I walked a very fine line just so I could make it through in one piece. When I made it on the bus for our winter championship HEPS meet, I finally felt like a Penn athlete.

At HEPS, I was set to run the mile race. The way the mile works is you run a preliminary race first, and athletes have to place first or second in their heat in order to move on to the finals. As a way to even out the competition, each heat has a combination of athletes with fast and slow mile times. I was not projected to make it to the finals since I had one of the slower times, and I went into the race as an underdog.

Throughout my time running I have become inherently aware of my internal clock. I know when a race goes out too fast or too slow. When the gun sounded the start of the race, we took off too fast, and my mind knew it too. In high school, my coach always told me, "Run your race." This phrase stuck with me throughout college. I was in last for a majority of the race, but a voice in my head told me, "This is your last chance."

As magical and odd as that may seem, I heard that voice. My mind knew the future before my physical presence even reached it. This really was my last opportunity to race. I took off and started to pass individuals each lap. I ended up winning the heat and making it to the final.

Despite the great race, the most captivating moment was watching the Penn track and field women's team win HEPS after a twenty-two-year hiatus. Ending winter track off a huge win made me excited for spring track, and I arrived at our first spring practice with the same energy and excitement.

One workout in particular included a 5,000-meter tempo run, which targeted both speed and endurance training. I had a great workout, hitting both my goal mile and 5K times. After the workout, though, my foot hurt. I shrugged it off because I was too excited about the great workout I just accomplished. Later that evening, I received a text from my coach telling me he was excited for me and the potential I had for the season. I was ecstatic to hear that from him, as I have always looked up to him and appreciated his kindness and patience during my many injuries.

This excitement was cut short, though, after feeling the throbbing pain in my foot once again, this time stronger and for a longer duration. I decided to pay a visit to my favorite doctor that week to check in on my symptoms. After listening to my history of injuries, she decided I should get an MRI to rule out a stress fracture. I was going to miss the opening race of the season, but I stayed hopeful that I just had tendonitis.

The opening meet of the spring track season took place at Franklin Field, and a few local Philadelphia colleges came to participate. My friends on the team were gearing up for the mile race, and soon cheers and yelling indicated the start of the races and field events.

During all of the excitement and admiration for track and field, I had to leave. It hurt too much to sit there, sidelined once again. This was my fifth time waiting on an MRI diagnosis on whether or not my running career was over. It was painful watching the race I was supposed to be in, and the sport I loved so much, from a distance.

I left the track and slowly walked up Locust Street. I was not sure what to do with myself, so I texted my best friend Samantha. "Do you want to study in the Law Library today?" I had to busy my mind with something other than running. "Yes, should we get Starbucks beforehand?" I was not just tasting the coffee that Saturday, but also a day in the life of just a student. Not a student athlete.

ONE WEEK LATER:

A week after both the MRI and the opening meet of the season, my foot was feeling better. I was hopeful that the pain I felt was just a brief period of tendonitis. I was getting ready to leave for my follow-up appointment with my doctor when I decided to pack myself some gloves and a headband in anticipation that I would be cleared to run.

I had begun my descent down Locust Walk when I saw a few students running. I smiled, feeling both hopeful and excited that I would soon be joining them. I reached the doctor's office and was told to take a seat. My mind drifted: "I think I will run on the Schuylkill River today." There was a knock on the door, and I told the doctor she could enter. I could tell she had bad news by the way she walked in: a solemn face, with a slowed, steady entrance. "How much pain are you in?" she asked, and then proceeded to tell me I had a stress fracture.

I didn't cry. I told her thank you and left the office to go see my trainer for a boot...once again. And then I really left, both Franklin Field and the sport of track and field.

I didn't know what to do with myself, so I went to a window seat I love at the Fisher Fine Arts Library on Penn's campus. I sat there, looking up at the beautiful architecture and down at the students focused on something that had nothing to do with running. Yet, I personally felt my whole existence had gone away as if I had lost it.

I put my baseball cap on and left the library. There was a heavy rain coming from the sky, yet I continued to pull out my phone to call my dad. "What's wrong, Kylene?" Through watery eyes and a clogged throat, I told him, "My collegiate running career is over." My heart was broken. My collegiate running career was over, and I was expected to just take this news and accept it?

I knew that while my mind loved the sport, my body just couldn't handle finishing the race.

I was in my dorm room unpacking my backpack when I came across the gloves I had packed the day prior, in anticipation that I could run again. I stared at them on my bed and fell into the emotion. At that point I laid down and just cried for a while. It was hard for me to look outside the window and see Franklin Field and not be frustrated and sad that I would no longer wear the stripes of Penn. The feeling I had racing under the lights was over. Three-fifteen p.m. will continue to strike, and I will always be reminded of the significance of this time; I was granted an opportunity to just run, in great company and under great guidance.

After I allowed myself to be vulnerable and let out the pain, I went outside. The sun was hitting the buildings in such a way I could stare at them and not feel blinded. I was able to look into the light, God's symbol that everything was going to be all right.

The HEPS winter race that year was the last time I had ever put on the Penn uniform. That voice in my head was my intuition; my mind knowing more about me than I realized. No race should ever be taken for granted. I replay my last race at times in my mind, and I remember how gritty I was, and how excited I was to go fast. That was my last sensational taste for the exhilarating and momentous emotion I felt when racing.

And with all this realization, you ask, what has injury granted me? Vulnerability. Do not underestimate the power of vulnerability, of tears, and of raw emotions. Feeling these emotions indicates you are alive, and that you feel the moment. Injury allowed me to count my blessings while simultaneously discovering new ones. Injury allowed me to truly understand how to live...in the moment.

Since my graduation at the University of Pennsylvania, I had not stepped foot in Franklin Field. It was difficult for me to look at the place where I spent so much time sidelined.

This removed presence from Franklin Field occurred until graduate school. It was a late September or early October night when I returned back to the track I had loved so much. I was with a friend, and we had just finished up a workout next door at Drexel's gym. Since Penn was across the street, I felt this desire to show him my previous home the past four years. Walking onto Franklin Field, we watched as the flag football team finished up its practice. The night had a slight hint of summer, but there was a beautiful breeze that was familiar to fall. We eventually went to the very top of the bleachers and just looked at the view of the city and the stars, fully immersed in the moment.

This time around in Franklin Field, I was not awaiting the workout for the day, nor was I warming up on the infield for my future race. I was feeling weightless and fullness in something apart from running, my personality.

Seated in Franklin Field, I was talking about my passion as a future physical therapist. I looked down on the bleachers I used to sit on and just smiled. I reflected back on my freshman-year self and how much I had yet to learn about myself.

My experience undergoing five different injuries in four years allowed me to reflect on a once-painful moment as a powerful one. I overcame those dark days, those cold pool workouts, and those frequent doctor visits. I was now living the life that existed outside the running one. How remarkable, how lucky am I to have experienced both lives? To have fully given everything I had to running, and yet still have untouched life still left to live?

My experience running at UPenn was a moment. A pure, emotional, viable, beautiful moment. I captured it, I lived it, I overcame it. **I was broken then, but I was Unfinished with what life still has to offer.**

CHAPTER FIFTEEN:

LIFE IN THE BETWEEN

I Was an Actress.
In The Beginning, I Gambled with Guilt, and was Provided Healing Words.
I held an Obsessive Identity until
I discovered a New Mindset,
And became Energized.
Reflecting on my Younger Misconceptions,

I Listened with Grace.
I utilized Mental Imagination.
Becoming Selfishly Selfless
I found my Present Identity.
I re-lived My Last Run
And unveiled the Life in *the* Between.

***

The titles of my book chapters are my journey, **an unfinished product**. Perhaps an understanding that each struggle, discovery, and peaceful encounter is a chapter of a book. I asked myself, how do I end this book? How do you end the journey that is unfinished? It was not until I was home for an extended period of time that I truly felt present enough to end "The Unfinished Race."

Due to the 2020 COVID-19 pandemic, I lived at home with my three younger siblings and parents while attending my virtual PT classes. I was finishing up finals and commencing my final year of physical therapy graduate school.

With a few days off, I decided to clean out my room, starting with my closet. Anytime I clean out my room it takes me hours as I come across old letters or my old cell phone and get ensnared by distant memories. This time around, I found a large box pushed toward the way back of my closet. Reaching between the racks of clothes and old yearbooks, I grappled with the box and placed it into my lap. Brushing off the dust that had nestled its way on top, I opened the battered box to see, with tear-filled eyes and peaceful wonder, what was left of my running life: my old racing spikes.

Gracefully taking out each pair, I recollect on the exact year I wore the spike. Memories meet my mind with a melancholy feeling. "Run your race, Kylene," my high school coach shouts to me, as I trace the brand name on my first pair of running spikes with my finger.

With the final lap bell sounding, my stride increases, and I take the race as my own. "Great race! A couple of things. You don't have to respond to me when I yell your splits, and don't wave to your dad during the race." I reminisce on my first race with my coach, when running was still novel and innocent.

A few years older, and a few seconds faster, my college coach yells out, "You look strong," at a time of the race where I felt anything but strong. A majority of my collegiate spikes were left unmolded and shiny. These were the ones I never laced up due to injury.

Sitting there in my childhood room, feeling emotions flood back, I realized this finite love was put in a box. The tears and hours I spent cross-training and in doctors' offices are in this box with a heavy emotional reminder that my days running collegiately are over.

Why am I saying this? Because my time with something I loved was shortened and it did not have to be that way. Those many hours spent cross-training in the pool and on the bike are here in this box...in the back of my closet. Yes, I made it back always strong, and I even made it to some further meets, but I always got injured again...and again. My body continuously broke, yet I continued to only think of the race. I did not see injury as an opportunity to discover passion in something other than running, while simultaneously allowing my body to heal.

I wish I had prepared my mind and body to accept my injuries and take it slow.
I wish I had not trained as heavily during a time my body needed to heal.
I wish I had cultivated a harmonious passion earlier on.
I wish I had focused on preparing, arriving stronger, rather than racing to finish.

I truly believe had I improved my female athlete triad upon initial diagnosis I would have spent more time on the track. I would have felt more confident knowing my body was at a healthy weight for *me*. Everyone talks about a "healthy weight," but honestly think of weight as "(insert your name)'s weight." The weight that allows you to regulate monthly, a weight that allows you to have positive thoughts because you are not at an energy deficit, a weight that allows you to live this shortened life we have with happiness, and not one focused on calories or numbers.

Today, I know myself through my energy levels. I take such pride and appreciation when I feel "full." Full of happiness, love, nourishment, and my own personality. My personality can only radiate and shine when the people I associate with inspire me and love me for me. This fullness has transitioned me to a different lifestyle and direction; my current life is more attentive to my career and academia. I still love working out, focusing heavily on strength training. This mindset led me toward incredibly positive news this past summer after being told my bone density was great for my age. **I finally won the race!** This was the moment when I felt I was ahead.

In summary, I wrote this book because I wanted to tell the real-life stories of injury. I hope this book allows those injured to realize they are not alone. I hope after reading this book injury becomes a time to self-discover, rather than a time of identity loss.

The race is not finished, my friends. Even though I am done racing collegiately, I am still here, and I am still advocating for mental health, physical health, and pushing to transform the running world. But it is up to you as well! Support one another and recognize when someone needs to talk with you. Be the voice and the ear. I am looking forward to working with female athletes one day too as a physical therapist, and I hope to even coach high school track one day.

I will continue to advocate for the injured athlete and to promote the belief that recovering from injury is a multilayered process. I will check in with athletes during the injury process and tell them to validate *all* of their emotions. I will tell them the emotions they are feeling are normal, and together we can find ways to feel better as a complete person.

The truth of this book, though, is that I have yet to unlock my true potential. My potential sits in the box in the back of my closet, until I feel ready to lace back up. I want you all to unlock your true potential. Train your mind but build a body that is full. Allow yourself to grow and embrace injury with an open mind and an understanding that your body is telling you something.

I want to end with one last final thought. The track is continuous: a circle that endures with no finite ending. If you ever feel lost, think back to that circular track. Running competitively or not, you can always find your way back on track no matter the delays or disappointments you have faced. But before you lace up those spikes and toe that line, consider what you have learned and be sure to answer this question: Are you coming back stronger?

Despite the race for faster times, more goals accomplished, and higher jumps recorded, the race is always unfinished. The circles can continue on and on. Thus, we must focus on the importance of preparing to get on track. Why think about races and tasks completed, rather than moments prepared? The time you spend preparing are the times during which you mold your identity, your personality, and your passions.

I wish I had spent more time preparing, rather than thinking about finishing. The best moments in my life have never been finishing. I have never enjoyed finishing the morning's coffee, finishing the movie's popcorn, or finishing my favorite Italian dish, as much as I did preparing it. Even studying for exams, while I always felt better finishing the exam, I gained the most life skills and self-satisfaction from preparing for them.

The in-between aspects of life are the most virtuous and uplifting compared to the start and finish. The snuggles during the movie's intermission, the latte that is only half-way done, the anticipation at a restaurant before your meal is served. All the in-between moments are my favorite, but, having prepared them. No meal warmed in a microwave was ever held in grateful remembrance. The ones where I cooked and sautéed vegetables while listening to Frank Sinatra are always my favorite.

***

Take Away:

- Prepare yourself to start, my friends. The in-between, the running experience, will be all the better. Trust me.
- My race is unfinished, because to finish means I am attesting that I am done, that I know everything and have conquered everything.
- To be finished means I will never exhibit resilience again, that I will never have to dig for grit again during demanding times.
- To be finished means I am accepting the running world is perfect...and it is not.
- To be finished means I was done with the in-between: the real emotional values of life, of which I am still living.

ACKNOWLEDGEMENTS

I want to thank my family, the Cochrane Clan, for supporting me in this dream. Our days spent dancing in the kitchen allow me to know what true happiness and love feel like.

Thank you to my interviewees; your words and experiences granted me confidence and support to write this book:

Coach Juli Benson, Lauren Beecher, Jeff Copen, Sierra Castaneda, Chelsey Cochrane, Ryen Frazier, Debbie Gonzalez, Dana Klein, Liz Lansing, Nick McFarland, Jen Muller, Alison Nicolosi, Colette Richter, Laura Steel, Margaret Thomson, Julia Trethaway, Christiana Rutkowski.

Thank you to New Degree Press, especially Eric Koester, Brian Bies, and Jason Chinchen. Your advice throughout this book journey will always be remembered and appreciated.

A special thank you to Aunt Jane for reading this book in its entirety before it went to publishing.

Lastly, I want to thank the individuals who believed in me and ordered a book even before they had it in their hands. You allowed this dream to happen; I am eternally thankful.

Evelina/Steve Cochrane, Phyllis DeFranco, Thomas Lawrence, Matt Ferreri, Nicholas Mancini, Alexander Pachella, Lynne Gormley, Nicholas McFarland, Marc Lintal, Megan

Sellers, Jamie Golub, Linda Murphy, Marika Tsamutalis, Jean Farrell, Katie Culik, Danielle/Chris Cochrane, Thomas Connelly, Anna Peyton Malizia, Ryen Frazier, Nicole Macco, Jake Eberth, Maria Amante, Rachel Stremme, Sharon Dunn, Erin Egan, Julianna Catania, Caroline Larrabure, Samantha Miller, The Fealey Family, Michael and Susan Keating, Lorraine Fleming, Steven Mezzacappa, Julia Trethaway, Susanne Govan, Ian Gory, Philip Nicolosi, Fred Karaisz, Ava Ortiz, Brianna Chernes, Colette Richter, Diane DeOliveira, Victoria Valentino, Debbie Zgola, Zachary Zgola, Katie Rubright, Rita Voci, Lorraine Morelli, Caitlin Zgola, Jeremy Pittenger, Nick Kontos, Deb Caulfield, The Soltes Family, Karen Creamer, Jason Woodring, Doreen Csutoros, Christopher Bui, Kate Twilley, Jay Herrigel, Iverson Korsen, Daniel Cohn, Erica Capello, Holly Bischof, Ashley Warner, Kaitlin Fleming, Valerie Iovine, Carole Harsch, Marin Warner, Dana Harrington, Nicolas Shah, Kim Rainforth, Victor Cochrane, Annmarie Tarleton, The Boyd Family, Stephanie Miodus, Amanda Marasco, Ameer Almuaybid, Judy Murphy, Olivia Ryan, Abraham Gertler, Marc Grebelsky.

APPENDIX

Introduction:

National Collegiate Athletic Association. "NCAA Recruiting Facts: College Sports Create a Pathway to Opportunity for Student-Athletes." Updated August 2020. Accessed January 1, 2021. https://ncaaorg.s3.amazonaws.com/compliance/recruiting/NCAA_RecruitingFactSheet.pdf.

The New York Times. "I Was the Fastest Girl in America, Until I Joined Nike | NYT Opinion." November 7, 2019. Youtube Video, 6:59. https://www.youtube.com/watch?v=qBwtCf2X5jw&t=5s.

Chapter Two: The History of Female Running

CBS Boston. "A Boston Marathon First: Bobbi Gibb On Her History-Making Run." March 29, 2016. Youtube Video, 3:09. https://www.youtube.com/watch?v=W8yKILypImQ.

Lovett, Charlie. *Olympic Marathon: A Centennial History of The Games' Most Storied Race.* Westport: Praeger Publishers, 1997.

Olympic.org. "Statistics: Women at the Olympic Games." Accessed January 2, 2021. https://www.olympic.org/women-in-sport/background/statistics.

Chapter Three: The Beginning

Statuta, Siobhan M. "The Female Athlete Triad, Relative Energy Deficiency in Sport, and the Male Athlete Triad: The Exploration of Low-Energy Syndromes in Athletes." *Current Sports*

Medicine Reports 19, no. 2 (February 2020): 43-44. 10.1249/JSR.0000000000000679.

Chapter Four A: Gambling with Guilt

Duckworth, Angela Lee. "Grit: The Power of Passion and Perseverance." Filmed April 2013 at TED conference. TED video, 6:01. https://www.ted.com/talks/angela_lee_duckworth_grit_the_power_of_passion_and_perseverance?language=en.

Chapter Four B: Applying the Grit:

Duckworth, Angela Lee. "Grit: The Power of Passion and Perseverance." Filmed April 2013 at TED conference. TED video, 6:01. https://www.ted.com/talks/angela_lee_duckworth_grit_the_power_of_passion_and_perseverance?language=en.

Chapter Six: Obsessive Passion and Identity

de Jonge, Jan, Yannick A. Balk, and Toon W. Taris. "Mental Recovery and Running-Related Injuries in Recreational Runners: The Moderating Role of Passion for Running." *International Journal of Environmental Research and Public Health* 17, no. 3 (February 2020): 1044. https://doi.org/10.3390/ijerph17031044.

Chapter Eight: The Importance of Fueling One's Energy

Penn Athletics. "Women's Track and Field: Juli Benson." Accessed November 15, 2020. https://pennathletics.com/sports/womens-track-and-field/roster/coaches/juli-benson/2376.

Statuta, Siobhan M. "The Female Athlete Triad, Relative Energy Deficiency in Sport, and the Male Athlete Triad: The Exploration of Low-Energy Syndromes in Athletes." *Current Sports Medicine Reports* 19, no. 2 (February 2020): 43-44. 10.1249/JSR.0000000000000679.

Chapter Nine: Young Misconceptions

"American Physical Therapy Association." Association's Role in Advocacy for Prevention, Wellness, Fitness, Health Promotion, and Management of Disease and Disability: Policies and Bylaws. Last updated September 20, 2019. https://www.apta.org/siteassets/pdfs/policies/association-role-advocacy.pdf.

Chapter Ten: Listen with Grace

Laux, Philipp, Bertram Krumm, Martin Diers, and Herta Flor. "Recovery–Stress Balance and Injury Risk in Professional Football Players: A Prospective Study." *Journal of Sports Sciences* 33, no. 20 (2015): 2140-2148. http://dx.doi.org/10.1080/02640414.2015.1064538.

North Carolina State University Athletics. "2020 Cross Country Roster: Ryen Frazier." Accessed January 31, 2021. https://gopack.com/sports/cross-country/roster/ryen-frazier/9461.

Chapter Eleven: Mental Imagination

Schuster, Corina, Roger Hilfiker, Oliver Amft, Anne Scheidhauer, Brian Andrews, Jenny Butler, Udo Kischka, and Thierry Ettlin. "Best Practice for Motor Imagery: A Systematic Literature Review on Motor Imagery Training Elements in Five Different Disciplines." *BMC Medicine* 9, no. 75 (June 2011): 1-35. https://doi.org/10.1186/1741-7015-9-75.

Chapter Twelve: Selfishly, Selfless

Gulliver, Amelia, Kathleen M. Griffiths, and Helen Christensen. "Barriers and Facilitators to Mental Health Help-Seeking for Young Elite Athletes: A Qualitative Study." *BMC Psychiatry* 12, no. 157 (September 2012): 1-14. https://doi.org/10.1186/1471-244X-12-157.

Made in the USA
Middletown, DE
28 May 2021